C000151123

10014

DATE DUE

PRINTED IN U.S.A.

JOSLYN ART MUSEUM
ANCIENT GREEK POTTERY

By Ann Steiner

with a contribution by Charles Rowan Beye

Published by Joslyn Art Museum, Omaha, Nebraska

This project was made possible by generous grants from the National Endowment for the Humanities, a federal agency.

Published by Joslyn Art Museum, Omaha, Nebraska.

EDITOR: Ann Steiner
DESIGNER: Stephanie Knopp Designs, Lancaster, Pennsylvania
PHOTOGRAPHY: Photography Incorporated, Toledo, Ohio
COMPOSITION: Centennial Graphics, Inc., Lancaster, Pennsylvania
LITHOGRAPHY: Parke Duing Lithographers
          Steckel Printing, Inc.
          Lancaster, Pennsylvania

FRONTISPIECE: Symposium. Drawing of the exterior of a red-figure cup by the Ashby Painter, ca. 480 B.C. (London E 64, from Vulci).

COVER: A winged male chases a female. Attic red-figure Nolan amphora, ca. 450 B.C. (Joslyn 1965.407).

Library of Congress Cataloging-in-Publication Data

Joslyn Art Museum.
    Joslyn Art Museum: ancient Greek pottery.

    Bibliography: p.
    1. Pottery, Greek—Exhibitions. 2. Pottery, Ancient—Greece
—Exhibitions.   3. Joslyn Art Museum—Exhibitions. I. Steiner,
Ann, 1951–   .   II. Beye, Charles Rowan. III. Title.   IV. Title:
Ancient Greek pottery.
NK4623.04J675   1985   738.3′82′09380740182254   85-80559
ISBN 0-936364-15-7 (pbk.)

Table of Contents

Foreword by Henry Flood Robert, Jr. 7

Introduction by Ann Steiner 9

Part I

Greek Culture and the Joslyn Vases
by Charles Rowan Beye 13

Classical Archaeology and Greek Pottery at Joslyn
by Ann Steiner 23

Part II

Historical Development of Greek Pottery
by Ann Steiner 33

Catalogue
by Ann Steiner 39

Glossary of Shapes 90

Glossary of Terms 91

Chronological Chart 92

Bibliography 94

Foreword

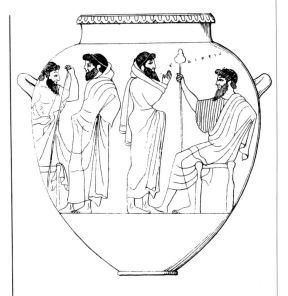

The Joslyn Art Museum has assembled its collection of ancient pottery over the past half century by both acquisition and donation. A significant proportion of the collection were gifts from members of the community, or were purchased with their help. Several pieces were formerly in two important local collections: those of George W. Lininger and Eugene Kingman, former Director of Joslyn. Most recently, in 1984, the museum acquired a group of vases on permanent loan from the Anthropology Division of the University of Nebraska State Museum in Lincoln.

The present exhibition, a permanent installation of the most significant pieces of Joslyn's ancient pottery, is one part of a comprehensive project conceived to make the collection available to both the general public and the scholarly community. The present catalogue is designed as a general resource. However, a separate more definitive catalogue of the vases, a fascicule of the *Corpus Vasorum Antiquorum*, will also be published and will enjoy a worldwide distribution through Philipp von Zabern of Mainz, West Germany. In anticipation of the exhibition and publications of the collection, ten vases were sent to Fogg Art Museum's Center for Conservation and Technical Studies for cleaning and restoration. The Center's work greatly enhanced the integrity and appearance of these vases so that they could be presented in their finest possible state to Joslyn visitors.

Several individuals deserve thanks for the roles each played in shaping and executing the present catalogue and exhibition. Dr. Ann Steiner, Steinman Assistant Professor of Classical Archaeology at Franklin and Marshall College, Lancaster, Pennsylvania, and Visiting Curator of Ancient Art at Joslyn, is a specialist in Greek vase-painting and pottery. She proposed the undertaking of a new exhibition and publication of the collection to me in the fall of 1980 and was primarily responsible for the project.

Two well-known scholars served as consultants to Dr. Steiner. A specialist in the field of Greek vase-painting, Dr. Dietrich von Bothmer, Chairman of the Department of Greek and Roman Art, The Metropolitan Museum of Art, New York, provided assistance during the planning phase of the project. Dr. von Bothmer had visited Joslyn during the 1950s and 1960s; he provided a great deal of information on the dating and attribution of pieces in the collection.

Dr. Charles Rowan Beye, Professor of Classics, Boston University, acted as a consultant for the interpretive aspects of the project, during both planning and implementation phases. He is the author of one of the introductory essays in this catalogue.

Theodore W. James, Associate Director for Art at Joslyn, played a significant role in attaining funds, overseeing technical details, and arranging the exhibition.

Other individuals also deserve thanks for their contributions: Berneal V. Anderson, Joslyn's Registrar, for her coopera-

tion in facilitating study of a collection which was largely in storage; Marsha V. Gallagher, Curator of Material Culture at Joslyn, for advice on the arrangement and scope of the exhibition; Dr. Richard D. De Puma of the University of Iowa's School of Art and Art History for the profile drawings of the pottery; Raymond M. Sess and Carl J. Schulz of Photography Incorporated, Toledo, Ohio, for painstaking photography; and Eileen Markson, Art and Archaeology Librarian at Bryn Mawr College for arranging access to the nineteenth-century line drawings which help to illustrate the catalogue.

Finally, generous grants from the National Endowment for the Humanities, during both the planning and implementation phases, have made possible the new installation of our vases and this accompanying catalogue. The publication of the Joslyn fascicule of the *Corpus Vasorum Antiquorum* was supported by The J. Paul Getty Trust and the National Endowment for the Arts. A National Endowment for the Arts grant was also instrumental in the conservation of a number of pieces in the collection.

Henry Flood Robert, Jr.
Director

Introduction

One purpose of this exhibition and catalogue is to present Joslyn's collection of ancient vases to the public. Another aim is to illustrate the methods which the classical archaeologist uses to study Greek pottery to acquire knowledge of the ancient past. Specifically, the design of both exhibition and catalogue is intended to acquaint the viewer with the history and development of Greek pottery, its uses and meaning in its original context, and its relationship to other expressions of ancient Greek culture.

Part I of the catalogue is an introductory section comprised of two essays. The first displays the many and diverse relationships between the Joslyn vases and other aspects of Greek culture, in particular the literary tradition. The second essay explains the study of Greek pottery as a discipline of classical archaeology, using the vases in Joslyn's permanent collection to illustrate methods which the archaeologist employs to extract information from material remains.

Part II of the catalogue is a series of short commentaries on individual pieces in the collection. An account of the historical development of Greek pottery prefaces this section; each entry which follows explains a piece and discusses the evidence which it yields. The arrangement of the entries in the catalogue matches the placement of the vases in the exhibition.

The line drawings which appear throughout the catalogue represent masterpieces of Greek vase-painting now in various museums throughout the world. They are reproduced from *Monumenti Inediti pubblicati dall'Instituto di Corrispondenza Archeologica* (Rome, 1829–91) except where noted otherwise. In the nineteenth and early twentieth centuries, before photography came into general use, scholars frequently illustrated vases by means of such drawings. Although the drawings may not be precise renderings, they are still of use to archaeologists; in some cases vases are now lost and such drawings are the only preserved visual record of the pieces. Many drawings are masterpieces of the engraver's art and they provide us with valuable documentation of the early history of the study of Greek vases.

An explanation of most specialized terminology which scholars of ancient pottery use is provided in the second introductory essay. However, two points need clarification at the outset: the names given to the parts of a vase correspond to the parts of the human body, from "mouth" to "shoulder" to "belly" to "foot." The primary side of a vase is called "A" or the "obverse" and the side of less importance, "B" or the "reverse." Chronological periods, names of individuals and places, and technical terms may be unfamiliar to some readers. Therefore, we provide a glossary, map, and chronological chart at the end of the catalogue for reference.

Ann Steiner
Visiting Curator of Ancient Art

Part I

Greek Culture and the Joslyn Vases

Charles Rowan Beye

The Joslyn collection offers an array of material which allows us to understand any number of aspects of Greek antiquity above and beyond the sorts which arise from the more narrowly focused study of art history and archaeology.

Themes

The ancient Greeks had a decidedly anthropocentric or "man-centered" view of things. The vases reflect this. The majority of the scenes on Greek vases show human beings rather than subjects from nature. This corresponds to the literary facts. We find almost no verbal descriptions of natural settings or things and no landscapes until the relatively late pastoral poems of Theocritus. Greeks never talk of going out in the countryside. The one occasion when Socrates is described in the *Phaedrus* as strolling out of Athens is remarkable. On Joslyn's vases we do, however, find the occasional representation of animals (Nos. 16; 18). The lions of No. 16 were probably a motif inherited from the Near East rather than a scene observed by the Greek artist from nature; by this time, lions no longer roamed Greece. The lion image is a commonplace of the Homeric poems where the poet makes considerable use of similes in which human fighting is compared to the depredations wrought by lions. The Lion Gate at Mycenae, so-called because the sculpture which surmounts it represents two lionesses rampant, is an architectural demonstration of this very important symbol from the heroic age. The marauding lion is perhaps Homer's most important metaphor for the human condition as it was experienced in the heroic age as well as for the natural energy of the fighting man. He can say of Herakles that he had the heart of a lion (*Iliad* 5.538) and he eloquently describes masculine martial violence in this simile:

> Rage took over Diomedes as that of a lion
> out among the sheep in the wild lands
> whom a shepherd has grazed, as the lion was
> leaping from the sheepfold but he
> did not kill him, but only made him mad.
> The shepherd cannot fight him off, but hides;
> and the sheep are forsaken, running to and fro
> and the lion rages, leaping over the fence again.
>
> (*Iliad* 5.136-142)

Combat

In a society dominated by males and masculine interests, it is not surprising to find military activity depicted on the vases. Greek history is characterized, unfortunately enough, by a continual recourse to armed conflict for the settlement of disputes, so much so that its representation in vase-painting is commonplace. But military activity often assumed a kind of spiritual or mythopoetic value for the males of that culture. We can see this in the way the ancient historians stressed war

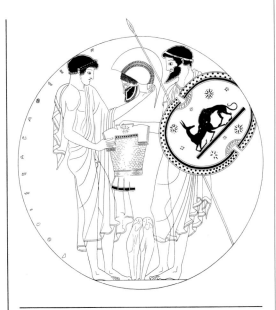

Figure 1. A warrior's essential equipment—helmet, corselet, greaves, spear, and shield.

Figure 2. "But when for the fourth time they had come around to the well springs
then the Father balanced his golden scales, and in them he set two fateful portions of death, which lays men prostrate,
one for Achilles, and one for Hector, breaker of horses, and balanced it by the middle; and Hector's death-day was heavier
and dragged downward toward death, and Phoibos Apollo forsook him." (**Iliad** *22.208-213. Translated by Richmond Lattimore)*

as a society's greatest achievement. Here on the vases, when the representation includes a chariot, the painter is making a statement about fighting. He is deliberately setting the scene hundreds of years before his time, since chariots were no longer used in conflict after the end of the Mycenaean era, c. 1200 B.C. The sixth-century B.C. painter who uses chariots in combat suggests to the viewer the heroic world, a time long since past, described by Homer in the epic poems *Iliad* and *Odyssey.* These two poems, memorized by countless schoolboys for centuries, kept the heroic ethos alive long after the age of the heroes had vanished. The men described in these two poems are confident, proud figures who found glory and fame, and hence a kind of immortality, triumphing in battle. Fighting was the way that they proved themselves and justified their existence. No. 22 is an example of this attitude as is No. 24 or No. 21.

The juxtaposition of the main scene of No. 17 with the shoulder decoration again describes the early heroic way of fighting, the aristocratic individualized warrior chieftain with his immensely expensive chariot and horses set against the general melee fighting hand to hand. That proud individuality, egoism, and self-aggrandizement are the very essence of heroism: in the *Iliad,* in the last glorious duel between Achilles and

Hector, as the former pursues the latter, Homer says:

> Great was the man who fled but his pursuer was greater still.
> Swiftly they ran since they ran not for prizes
> which are given to man in the contests of racing.
> No, but they ran for the prize of the life of horse-taming Hector.
> (*Iliad* 22.158-161)

These lines describe this moment of deadly combat almost as though it were an athletic contest. Indeed, for the ancient Greeks athletic contests became the peacetime equivalent of battle, a socialized way to satisfy their highly developed need for competition. No. 31 shows a youth at the moment of athletic victory being received by Victory herself. Victory in athletic contests seemed to promise some kind of transcendence and permanence through fame. The fifth-century B.C. Theban poet, Pindar, wrote a series of choral odes celebrating athletic victories in which he continually gives expression to this idea. A horse race at the contests held at Olympia, for instance, is glorified and elevated with these words:

> The fame of the Olympic contests looks out afar from the
>   racecourse
> of Pelops, where swiftness of feet is in contest
> and the high points of boldness and the struggle of strength.
> The winner all the rest of his life
> has honey-sweet good weather
> because of the contests. Nobility that goes on day after day
> is highest for mortals.   (*First Olympian Ode*, 93-100)

The reverse picture of Herakles and Athena on this vase reinforces the human scene by aligning it with events from the mythic, divine world. This juxtaposition is the pictorial equivalent of what we often find in the victory poems of Pindar and his contemporary Bacchylides, in their celebration of the young athletes of Greece where constant mythical allusion exalts the human triumph. In his thirteenth victory ode, for instance,

Figure 3. Priam, King of Troy, ransoms the body of his fallen son, Hector, from the triumphant and arrogant Achilles.

Figure 4. Victory, or "Nike," alights to offer a fillet, the victor's symbol, to a successful contestant.

Figure 5. Herakles, having hung his useless sword in a tree above, must use the strength and ingenuity of the athlete to overcome the Nemean lion.

Bacchylides evokes the mythological aura surrounding the human wrestling matches at the Nemean Games by describing the first contest there between Herakles and the lion. This semi-divine heroic man is an emblem of all the males who will rise to greatness through victory at Nemea:

> See how Perseus' descendant [Herakles]
> all clever, puts his heavy hand upon the savage
> lion. For the man slaying, shining bronze will
> not pierce the skin—the sword bends back.
> I tell you now that here someday Greek men
> will sweat in the contest of the pankration.

(Thirteenth Ode, 46-57)

It is interesting to note that the heroic motif appears on the oil vessels used frequently in funeral rites, No. 24. The implication is that regardless of the sex or status of the viewer or the deceased, he or she will find consolation in the grandeur or transcendence which allusion to the heroic world suggests.

Eros and Women

Sex, as one might imagine, was as popular as war with the men of ancient Greece. The ancients often quoted the love lyrics of Mimnermus which began:

> What is life, what is joy without golden Aphrodite?
> May I die when her pursuits no longer matter to me.

What is interesting is the complete freedom from inhibition which allowed the vase-painters to represent all aspects of this passion from the purely physical to the sentimental, as homosexual experience as well as heterosexual. Love, or probably more likely, pure erotic desire appears in the scene of a young man and woman being brought together by the winged Eros, the divine embodiment of sexual desire, No. 30. There is the possibly more sinister scene of a winged figure, either the personification of a wind or Eros, pursuing a maiden (No. 5) while a mantled youth, all-ignorant and unconcerned, occupies the other side of the vase. Will desire make her the young man's victim? Compare this to the scene of the evening drinking party on No. 16 made up of men and their courtesan women which describes a common social event in the life of an ancient Greek male. For as Demosthenes says (*Against Neaira* 59.122),

> we have courtesans for our pleasure, whores for the daily therapy of our body and wives for the legitimate creation of a family and the care of our household.

The perfume container No. 26, showing a woman standing in her house, reminds us of Homer's portraits of his women, almost all of them described in their houses. This represents the other side to the ancient Greek male's limited view of woman as sex object, wife, and homemaker. For as Hector says to Andromache, in the *Iliad* when she tries to give him advice on strategy as the war between the Greeks and Trojans grows more desperate:

> Go back to the house and get to your work
> with the loom and the spindle; see that your
> servant girls take up their tasks as well.
> But leave the fighting to the men . . .   (*Iliad* 6.490-492)

Figure 6. The seemly bride's head is modestly veiled and she carries a small jar of perfume in this marriage procession, accompanied by torchlight and music.

Figure 7. Indiscretion on the part of a proper woman was not tolerated: here, an outraged hero reacts to the discovery of a woman and her lover.

Beauty

Youthful male beauty was as much prized as the prowess of brawn and it is not surprising to find young men as the subject for the vase-painter. We may note No. 29 showing a youth on one side similar to the lad on No. 5; they are easily identified as young by the absence of facial hair. Beards for the ancient Greek males were part of the natural process, the natural and necessary insignia of one's sex, and yet their onset marked the end to the masculine beauty which Greeks cultivated. The poet Tyrtaeus hints at an unconscious desire to stay the process when he can write:

> All things become the young man,
> he is a wonder to men, beloved of women,
> while living, and yet a thing of beauty still
> when he falls in the vanguard of the battle line.

To old age, on the other hand, the Greeks conceded wisdom; the obverse picture on No. 29 shows a young man preparing to leave on a trip, traveling hat on his back, being addressed by the other figure, an older man. It could be a fifth-century B.C. Laertes and Polonius. As Solon said:

> Seven times seven years into a man's life
> he surpasses all greatly in his mind and his
> speaking power.

We of the twentieth century consider all Greek vases to be objects of art. Yet many like the oil container No. 25, were purchased initially for their contents. A mere container of this quality suggests a culture which sought beauty in everything and consciously kept to a standard. The language itself mirrors this, for the word for "beautiful," *kalos,* also means "good" implying that the ancient Greeks saw a moral imperative in creating beautiful things and in being beautiful. The beautiful oil containers are thus not unusual. One can compare them to the occasional attempts at fine packaging in our own era, such as the original Coca-cola bottle and equally aesthetically pleasing Kleenex box, as they were originally conceived decades ago long before commercial considerations perverted the original designs. In ancient Greece, by contrast, beautiful utilitarian vessels remained commonplace.

Aesthetics

The viewer will be struck by the painter's instinct to fill his surface. This is most apparent in vases of the Geometric period (No. 2) which have been compared often in their aesthetic impulse to the narrative style to be found in the *Iliad* and the *Odyssey*. Homer tells us everything, developing a remarkably detailed surface narrative, which leaves no surprises, nothing to be filled in by the reader. The same may be said for the Geometric vase where the painter clearly employs every part of his surface, again quite the opposite of Cezanne or Matisse whose effect often depends on the bare canvas. The impulse to use space appears again in later vase-painters in the form of space-fillers, such as the snake and bird found on No. 16.

Symmetry

No one who encounters ancient Greek culture will fail to notice the attention to form usually expressed by the recourse to symmetry which characterizes what has come to be called "classical." We might say that form, in its marriage with content, generally plays the dominant role. But the vase-painters who wrought so many careful borders and thereby fenced in

Figure 8. Two sons of Zeus, Castor and Polydeuces, return home to their parents, little groom, and pet.

Figure 9. In some cases, the decoration on the two sides of the vase is related: a flute-player performs on the obverse while a judge listens to him on the reverse.

and framed their scenes, occasionally showed a highly developed sense of the integrity of the scene displayed, allowing it of necessity to spill over onto the border area. In No. 24 for instance, the lofty plumes of the helmets of the warriors protrude up above the scene into the key pattern and the painter even suggests depth by the way he has painted them in front of the decorative border.

Antithesis

The integration we have just discussed contrasts with the commonplace disinclination to organize the scenes of the vase into an organic whole. Again and again we might note that the scene on one side of the vase has nothing to do with that on the other, as No. 21. This tendency, however, might be considered a pictorial version of the well-known verbal or logical tendency of the ancient Greeks to pose things in antithesis. There is probably no other habit of mind so fundamental to ancient Greece. It is inherent in almost everything, tragedy, for instance, or post and beam construction, or even Aristotle's law of the excluded middle (everything is either A or not A). The way in which Greeks described their culture is also profoundly antithetical; one thinks of Achilles and Odysseus, tragedy and comedy, Athens and Sparta, or Greeks and barbarians. Even the most common Greek sentence structure makes its statement "on the one hand" and "on the other hand." *Parataxis,* as this is called, is similar to the presence of unrelated scenes on the same vase.

Once we have acknowledged, however, what is a clearly established tendency to dissociate scenes on vases, we the present day viewers, conditioned to believe in the importance of word association as Freud defined it, will tend to notice combinations which make visual sense to us. Such an instance is No. 17 where the shoulder illustration portrays Amazons, Herakles in the center, duelling, while the main scene represents heroic men, their chariot and horses. Specifically, these have nothing to do with one another, and the habit of the painter, studied on his other vases, is to make no connection. Yet visually, the overall painting suggests all the elements of one battle.

No. 4 provides an interesting speculation. The scene of the athlete (not a warrior: there are no weapons) harnessing his chariot seems to be related to the shoulder illustration of a man stepping into his chariot. We would like to see a narrative connection between these two scenes, especially because of their juxtaposition. Yet they both are exceedingly commonplace illustrations, occurring again and again on other vases with clearly no relation to the other scenes set beside them so that we are forced to consider that the two scenes here are in fact only so much decoration, pattern more than narrative. On the other hand, sometimes the scene suggests the function of the container, as for instance, the scene of the wine god Dionysos on a drinking cup, No. 20, or depictions of women laying a wreath on a tombstone on white-ground funerary vessels, No. 27.

Analysis

Another characteristic of the Greek mind which is readily apparent from an examination of the Joslyn vases is what has been called "the early Greek capacity for viewing things separately." The Geometric vase No. 2 is an early example of this relatively long-lived intellectual tendency among the Greeks. Here we may note that the neck, body, rim and base of the vase have been insisted upon as separate entities by the painter's use of linear elements which isolate and make panels of the various parts of the vase. The birds which are illustrated are divided up into parts, even the toes are significantly articulated. When we look at this piece we do not see "bird"; the painter has made us concentrate instead on each part of the vase, each feature of the bird, as separate but equal features. Similarly, the vase No. 22 from the Archaic period has many imposingly defined elements: for instance the linked lotus buds which set off the top of the rim; the palmettes which do the same for the handle plates; the ivy pattern on the side of the rim; the tongues on the shoulder, and so on. The painted panels themselves are set off and framed by more ivy. The various architectural elements of this vase are not orchestrated into a whole. They are decorated emphatically exactly so as to emphasize their singularity. This is the same aesthetic impulse which so carefully delineates—almost as if counting them—the legs of the horses in the painting on this vase.

If we turn to other aspects of Greek culture we can remark on innumerable other instances of this overriding analytical habit of intellect. Doric architecture, for instance, establishes, through a variety of shapes and by painting, separately articulated elements such as the capital, the architrave, the metopes, the triglyphs, the pediment and so forth. Ancient Greek tragic drama was unvaryingly divided into dialogue passages with individual speakers and choral passages sung and danced as a group. This latter element at fixed intervals interrupted the flow of the dramatic action in exactly the same divisive way that the decoration of these vases inhibits our seeing them whole. The characteristic reappears in the first real intellectual Greece produced, the historian Thucydides, whose account of the Peloponnesian War is marked by a constant shift between detailed battle narrative and speculative generalizing speeches which almost stand in counterpoint, the event enacted and the perception of the thing experienced. So it is that the Greeks' penchant for *analysis*—their own word—is to be found everywhere, establishing the foundation for the philosophical thought of Plato, Aristotle, and their successors.

Clearly the Joslyn vases offer us the means to reflect upon a variety of trends in ancient Greek culture, both in the themes which are represented and the way in which decoration is organized on the vessel.

Figure 10. Greek intellectuals wrote on and read from scrolls as illustrated here.

Classical Archaeology and Greek Pottery at Joslyn

Ann Steiner

Classical archaeology is a discipline devoted to the study of the material remains of ancient Greek and Roman cultures. Its essential purpose is to correct and supplement our picture of the past derived from the preserved writings of ancient poets, tragedians, historians and public record keepers. Its approach is interdisciplinary, for the classical archaeologist strives to integrate a picture of the ancient past by considering relationships between different modes of cultural expression, such as the connections between art and literature demonstrated by Professor Beye in the previous essay. Although rigorously scientific in method, classical archaeology is primarily humanistic. Its purpose is to reach an understanding of human expression and effort during the nascent period of our own civilization.

The study of Greek pottery is just one of the many interdependent disciplines which combine to form classical archaeology. From an objective assessment of pottery, the classical archaeologist is able to reconstruct not only chronology and economics, but elements of myth and religion, daily life, and, of course, aesthetic standards. As a result, we learn a great deal about ancient Greek culture through pottery.

Rank

At the outset, it is necessary for us to define the role and rank of Greek pottery in relation to other categories of art. Some examples of Greek pottery are certainly what is called "monumental art": creations meant to impress and to endure. Some vase-painters were certainly masters who produced masterpieces, although in antiquity potters and vase-painters were paid and regarded more as craftsmen than "artists," just as were the sculptors, architects, and poets. Often vases, just as sculpture and architecture, were used as dedications in sanctuaries and may have been made for that purpose.

However, Greek vases are in certain respects different from monumental arts. Vases were made to be sold, in most cases, with no particular buyer in mind; nearly all sculptures, architecture, and wall-paintings were made by commission. There were unique commercial considerations which affected pottery-

Figure 11. This scene depicts vase-painters at work, inspired by Athena and her attendant victories. Note that a woman is among the craftsmen, at the far right. Reproduced from **History of Ancient Pottery** *by H. B. Walters (1905) p. 223.*

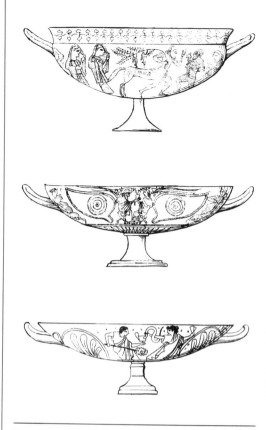

Figure 12. These three examples demonstrate the development of the Attic cup from deep and full to flat and shallow.

making, such as the need to package a particular product, or to reach a certain market. Pottery is certainly more ephemeral and smaller in scale than monuments in bronze or stone. Unlike any other category of art, pots were made to be used in daily life, to meet ordinary domestic needs, such as the storage and serving of food, whether at regular meals or on special occasions.

Shape

Although thousands of Greek vases survive, there is a very limited number of shapes which function primarily to store and serve liquids and solids. Astonishingly, many shapes in this limited repertory are established during the Geometric period (900–700 B.C.) and remain essentially the same until the beginning of the Hellenistic period (323-31 B.C.); this is a total of nearly 600 years. For examples of this continuity in the Joslyn collection, compare the Geometric cup No. 8 to the classical red-figure cup No. 30.

This conservatism and limitation of types are characteristically Greek approaches to the problem of dealing with change in human experience. In many spheres Greeks settle on a few types and work consciously or unconsciously toward their perfection. Also, Greeks tend to use one type for a multitude of purposes. This phenomenon is expressed most eloquently in the monumental arts, in the development of the representation of the ideal athlete, or in the evolution of the Doric temple. Just as the Doric order could be used in either religious, domestic, or civic architecture, the same vase shape was appropriate to hold grain, water, or wine in a sanctuary, house, or marketplace. Within an essentially conservative framework there is always room for individual inspiration (note the unusual hydria No. 17) and especially for practical improvements. The aims in the creation of pottery shapes are certainly aesthetic and might be dictated by religious necessity, but are primarily functional.

When scholars study ancient Greek pottery, they might begin by making an objective assessment of shape. Often this is accomplished with the help of a profile drawing, such as are included in this catalogue (see Nos. 32–34).

The names of the shapes may be transliterations of Greek terms (amphora: "carried on both sides," or hydria: "water vessel"), names found in literary sources and vase inscriptions. Lacking ancient evidence we have assigned certain shapes nicknames, made up on the basis of presumed function or by modern analogy. An example of the latter is the practice of calling very small bowls "saltcellars," when we do not know for certain that they were used to hold spices at table. Scholars are especially interested in the development of particular shapes for use in dating. In the Joslyn collection the development of the cup over a century can be discerned by comparing the following four examples: Nos. 15; 18; 20; 30. Note that the cup develops from a deep, full bowl to a much flatter, more shallow bowl.

Decoration

Decoration on vases includes subsidiary zones of ornament which are often non-figural or contain only animals as well as major narrative scenes.

Artists

Scholars attempt to discern the hands of particular artists and to assign works to these individuals. Most of the work in this area was completed by the late British scholar, Sir John Beazley. To make attributions to artists, he used what is called "Morellian analysis." This system, developed by a nineteenth-century art historian, Giovanni Morelli, relies on a comparison of small details in the rendering of features, dress, and pose to determine a particular painter's style. If the painter has signed any of his works, we learn his name from the signature; more commonly, the painter is assigned a nickname based on some aspect of his style or the location of one of his important works. Note, for example, No. 13 by the Joslyn Painter and No. 16 by the Omaha Painter.

For an example of how Morellian analysis works, compare the figures of the two amphoras, No. 5 and No. 29; the former is unattributed and the latter is assigned to the workshop of the Painter of London E 342. On the reverse of each stands a youth: each is draped, holds a staff, and stands on a key pattern ground line. Close inspection of details reveals differences in rendering; the eye of the youth on No. 5 is much larger and much closer to the line of the forehead than that on the figure on No. 29. There is a distinctive hook where the nose meets the upper lip on the former, which is lacking on the latter. The lines indicating drapery folds are straight or contain "U"-shaped curves on No. 5 while they can be wavy and serpentine on No. 29. There are no details of ankle bones on the latter figure, while both are preserved on the former. Thus, by a comparison of details we may conclude that the two figures are not by the same painter, despite the apparent similarities.

Once the identity of an artist is determined, a number of pieces may be assigned to him. Scholars then may study the tastes and preferences of an artist by looking at his repertory of subject matter and shapes. Such studies provide our earliest opportunity to analyze the *oeuvres* of individual painters in Western civilization.

Interpretation of Scenes

When scholars have organized the material into a relative sequence for each geographical area and divided it into particular hands or workshop groups, they use the pottery to interpret various other aspects of Greek culture.

To achieve the proper assessment of the depictions on Greek pottery is one of the most difficult tasks which faces archaeologists and art historians, and many of the problems still remain to be solved.

Early in the history of the study of vases, scholars interpreted scenes on Greek pottery as "illustrations" of Greek literature. While there is certainly some correspondence between

Figure 13. A comparison of Nos. 5 and 29 demonstrates the subtleties of Morellian analysis.

Figure 14. This scene may depict an actual historical figure, King Croesus of Lydia in Asia Minor, seated on his funeral pyre.

famous scenes from Greek epic and the works of the great tragedians and what appears on vases, this theory only serves to explain a small selection of preserved representations.

In some cases, depictions on pottery are surely derivatives of major artistic creations other than literary efforts. This is a phenomenon observed frequently in several categories of ancient art: less expensive, smaller scale items often imitate larger, well-known monuments. We see the reproduction of monumental sculpture in both terracotta figurines and on coins. Monumental sculpture also appears to have influenced the iconography of Greek pottery, although perhaps not as directly. In the second half of the fifth century B.C. we see both reflections of the sculpture of the Parthenon and the works of the sculptor Polykleitos on vases.

Certainly there is a correspondence between representations on vases and the myths of the Greeks: for example, in the Joslyn collection, we see fights with Amazons and the activities of heroes and gods. These ought not be regarded as illustrations of literary accounts of myth, but really as parallel ways to express myth, visual rather than verbal. Moreover, representations of myths, as far as we may tell, do not account for anywhere near all depictions on Greek pottery. A more difficult problem is the distinction between representations of myth and the religious cults with which they are associated. For example, in the scenes involving Dionysos (Nos. 19–21) do we see a purely mythical scene or in some cases do we see mortals practicing the cult of Dionysos as well?

This leads us to the vexing problem of evaluating scenes from daily life. We assume that such scenes had to be close enough to reality to be meaningful, and the realistic representation of the human figure, weapons, and armour encourages us to see such scenes as reliable reproductions of human activity. Moreover, there are demonstrable cases where political events seem to have influenced iconography on vases. We also know that artists were constrained by their medium, and that the Greek mentality preferred consistent artistic solutions in the same way that it preferred a limited number of types of all things. Compare, for example, the overwhelming similarity between the poses of the two female figures in the scenes on our two funerary lekythoi. Both show activity of real life, yet No. 27 is in a funerary context, while No. 28 is domestic. Many recent studies suggest that painters far preferred following long-established iconographical traditions to making fresh observations of daily life.

Caution, then, is of the utmost necessity in using the representations themselves as a source for understanding Greek culture. We must avoid intrepreting the scenes as photographs. They are very informative, though on a subtler level than mere literal interpretation allows.

Religion

Although they must exercise caution, some archaeologists are successful in interpreting a great deal about the religion of the ancient Greeks from the scenes painted on pottery. Gods

Figure 15. Athena, wearing helmet, her protective aegis—a goatskin with snakes at the borders—, shield, and spear. She appears here on an amphora given as a prize to victors in the Panathenaic Games, contests celebrated in honor of the goddess every four years at Athens.

and heroes appear on a number of Joslyn's vases and may be identified by the standard attributes which they wear or carry. These attributes represent each god or hero's distinctive characteristics. In this respect we see the same sort of standardization and reduction to essentials noted in the shape of Greek vases, for particular gods and heroes appear in consistent ways over long periods of time. On the kyathos No. 19, we may identify the messenger god Hermes by his broad-brimmed traveling hat, short cloak, and winged shoes, all of which help him to accomplish his required tasks. On the same piece, we identify the god Dionysos by his hairband of ivy leaves, long pointed beard, and spotted garment which recalls an animal skin. Dionysos is a nature divinity whose worship allowed men to pass the barrier from "civilized" behavior to "natural" behavior, so a crown of leaves and an animal skin garment are especially appropriate. He often carries a drinking vessel because his cult celebrates the production of wine. Note the similar way which the god appears on Nos. 20 and 21. Athena, as seen on No. 31, is a goddess associated with the arts of war. Fittingly, she wears a helmet and carries a spear.

Similarly, we may identify the hero Herakles in heroic combat with the Amazons on the shoulder of No. 17 and on Olympus, being poured a libation by his patron goddess Athena, on No. 31. We identify Herakles by his lionskin and by the club which he carries. The lionskin armour and the club amplify the fact that Herakles is, like many Greek heroes and divinities, savage and primitive in certain respects. Yet, by the context of both examples, we see that Herakles is a combination of opposites. He is a civilizing agent both in his battle against the barbarian Amazons and as a paradigm for athletic victory.

Daily Life

Some scenes do show the activities of daily life. At least two forms of entertainment appear on our vases: dancers who wear padded garments to exaggerate bellies and thighs (No. 15) and the symposium, where men are eating on dining couches while being entertained by female companions (No. 16). A simple domestic scene of a woman standing indoors appears on No. 26. No. 21 depicts mortal men preparing for battle.

Much of our evidence for funerary custom comes from the special class of white-ground lekythoi, as No. 27. Here the

Figure 16. Herakles, wearing his lionskin, uses his club and bow to fight the barbarian Amazons.

funerary monument closely resembles actual stone monuments which are preserved. A woman decorates the tombstone of a loved one with a garland.

A curious juxtaposition of a mortal athlete being greeted by the mythological personification of Victory appears on No. 31. Apparently this sort of combination of the mortal and divine spheres was not problematic for the Athenians, but emphasizes to us that we must interpret scenes of "daily life" with care.

Development of Realism

One of the major contributions of the Greek tradition to western art is that it accomplishes the shift from forms represented abstractly to those represented realistically. This development from abstraction to naturalism is well-represented within the Joslyn collection. Compare the Geometric bird on No. 2 to the more realistic swans on No. 16; likewise, compare the padded dancers on No. 15 to the victorious youth on No. 31. Specifically, the advancement in the rendering of a three-quarters pose may be seen by comparing the more abstract warrior on side A of No. 16 where the frontal torso combines with profile legs and head, to the left figure on the exterior of No. 30, where the figure turns at the waist more realistically. A comparison of the female figures on each piece demonstrates another example of the advancement of perspective in natural rendering.

Dating

The sequence of Greek pottery has very practical applications for the archaeologist and ancient historian. As mentioned above, developments in shape may be traced; this, together

Figure 17. This all-male symposium includes musicians: a lyre-player, and a flutist. Note kylikes, skyphos, and an oinochoe below.

Figure 18. A comparison of Nos. 16 and 30 demonstrates the development—over less than a century—of the Greek artist's ability to depict human figures realistically.

with the evolution of figural decoration provides a relative chronology which the circumstances of recovery can link to an absolute sequence. For example, a coin, safely dated by both archaeological and historical evidence, will date the pottery found with it. Similarly, a known historical connection to a particular monument dates the pottery associated with that monument. The black-figure lekythos, No. 25, attributed to the manner of the Haimon Painter, can be dated to the period around 475 B.C. for the following reasons: in shape and style the Haemonian workshop clearly descends in part from the work of the Marathon Painter. The lekythoi of the Marathon Painter are found in the collective burial of the Athenians who fell against the Persians at the Battle of Marathon in 490 B.C. Thus combining our knowledge of the relative sequence of shape and decoration with the historical record, we know that the Haemonian lekythos in Joslyn's collection must date after the Marathon burial.

Undecorated pottery is also useful as a dating tool. Black-glaze pottery produced in Athens from 450 B.C. to 300 B.C. (Nos. 32–34) was a cheaper alternative to figural ware and is found in great quantities both at Athens and in many provincial sites. It is particularly useful because we have abundant evidence for both its relative and absolute dates and because its appearance is so widespread.

Commerce

Pottery provides ancient historians with evidence of the commercial and economic picture of the Classical world. One example of this is reflected in the responsiveness of the Athenian potters to the demands of the Etruscan market. Early on, Attic craftsmen developed a class of pottery called "Tyrrhenian" as No. 16. Because these amphoras are found only in Italy, scholars believe that the shape was developed exclusively for export to Etruria. It has been suggested that the decorative scheme consciously evokes that of Corinthian pottery which had enjoyed enormous commercial success in Italy during the preceding century.

Later, toward the end of the sixth century B.C., Attic potters added to their repertory a shape copied from Etruscan potters: the kyathos, No. 19, is an example of this phenomenon. Again, this shape was marketed mainly in Etruria. A reversal of this trend may be seen when Etruscan potters imitate mainland products, such as the Italo-Corinthian example No. 13, in the sixth century.

A general history of the development of Greek pottery and more specific interpretations which apply to individual pieces in the collection follow. Above all, it is important to remember that Greek pottery is utilitarian, intended for daily use by ordinary individuals. Vases are recovered from graves, civic centers, religious shrines, and houses. At the same time, the high aesthetic standards, apparent in shape and decoration of its pottery, reflect the great achievements of Greek civilization.

PART II

Historical Development of Greek Pottery

Ann Steiner

The production of Greek pottery spanned many centuries; in the Joslyn collection there are pieces which represent over 1000 years of continuous pottery production. During this period we are able to observe distinctive phases, characterized by style and technique, similar to the divisions in modern art such as Impressionism and Cubism. The following summary is intended to provide an outline of these phases and their definitive characteristics.

Bronze Age: 3000–1100 B.C.

Bronze Age potters were expert craftsmen. Much of their subject matter was taken from nature; their tradition was a conservative one, and mainland potters received many of their motifs from their Cretan predecessors. While Cretan potters usually placed natural motifs so as to emphasize the vessel as a whole, the mainland potters typically subjected motifs to more rigid syntax which emphasized the individual parts of the vessel. No. 1 is an example of a mainland piece which uses a natural motif, the octopus, and emphasizes the vertical axis of the piece by the placement of the body of the sea creature. Such pottery was produced in a number of different centers and was exported to other parts of the Mediterranean.

Dark Age: 1100–900 B.C.

The collapse of Mycenaean civilization brought the production of the major arts and manifestations of culture to an end. Although the creation of monumental painting and architecture stopped, pottery production continued and is the single continuous aspect of material culture which we have for the Dark Age. Dark Age pottery, called "Protogeometric," is not represented in the Joslyn collection.

Geometric: 900–700 B.C.

In the Geometric Age, when we see the regeneration of a more advanced level of culture, pottery production picked up in intensity. Athens and the surrounding region, called "Attica," became the center of the craft. Attic potters initiated a position of dominance in the production of Greek pottery which they maintained with only a short hiatus until the fourth century B.C. Several technical innovations helped to improve the quality of pottery: a faster potter's wheel, allowing shapes to be tauter and more refined; the compass, which allowed circular elements to be painted with precision; and the multiple brush, an instrument which may have resembled a comb with brushes at the ends of the teeth, which was used to paint even rows of lines. The Geometric style, as the name implies, is characterized by the use of linear and circular elements, in dark paint on a light background. The individual decorative elements are arranged in horizontal and vertical zones which emphasize the structure of the vessel; the princi-

Figure 19. Animals appear in plastic form as well as two-dimensionally on Geometric pottery: three horses decorate the lid of this round container.

ple behind this system of decoration is similar to that seen earlier on Bronze Age vessels from the mainland. By about 800 B.C. animals entered the repertory, and by 750 B.C. human figures were present as well. The human and animal subjects were also represented in a geometric style, in silhouette. Nos. 2 and 8 have typical features of Greek Geometric pottery. Another example, No. 7, shows the Geometric style as it appeared in the contemporary pottery of Cyprus.

Orientalizing: 700–600 B.C.

By around 700 B.C., potters at Corinth had established it as the center of pottery production. The seventh century was a crucial moment in the development of Greek pottery, for it was the first time since the Bronze Age that any type of Greek pottery achieved both high technical expertise and widespread distribution throughout the Mediterranean. The Corinthians used motifs in large part acquired from the Near East; they developed the black-figure technique, characterized by the use of dark figures against a light background. Details in black-figure are indicated by incision, a process of using a very sharp instrument to engrave the clay before it is fired. Added red and white paint indicate other details. Subjects include stylized animal and vegetal motifs: Nos. 10–12. Some decoration implies a narrative, as the marching foot soldiers on No. 9 suggest.

Scenes of myth identified by inscriptions appeared during this period. This is a landmark in the history of Western art, for the appearance of narrative subjects may be closely linked to the development of realistic renderings of man and nature in art.

Corinthian pottery was widely exported and dominated markets commercially. It was imitated in the West, as a comparison between Nos. 12 and 13 indicates.

Figure 20. Sphinxes—winged felines with female heads—are part of the Near Eastern repertory acquired by the Corinthians.

Archaic-Classical: 600–400 B.C.

Figure 21. A heroic battle represented in the black-figure technique.

Black-Figure

In the early years of the sixth century B.C., Athenian craftsmen once again rose to the fore and dominated the pottery industry, both commercially and artistically. Not only did the Athenians overtake the Corinthian markets, they also took the black-figure technique and elements of style and iconography from the Corinthians. Some Corinthian potters actually may have emigrated to Athens, at the invitation of the Athenian leader Solon. Although the Athenian product relied on the inheritance from Corinth, it was distinct from its predecessor. The peculiar reddish-orange Athenian clay contrasted with the Corinthian buff, and Athenians used motifs differently. Representation of myth became much more common. Note the use of the Corinthian animal frieze in the Attic repertory by comparing No. 12 with Nos. 16 and 18. No. 15 is an example of technique, shape, and subject matter taken over from the Corinthians.

Attic black-figure continued to develop along independent lines until it reached its height of artistic achievement at about 540 B.C. No. 17 is an excellent example of the black-figure technique at its finest. This pottery was highly prized and widely exported, particularly to Etruria.

Red-Figure

Technical innovations changed the course of Athenian pottery at about 530 B.C. The Attic red-figure technique dictated a reversal of color scheme, where figures are reserved in the natural color of the clay and the background is painted black. This increases the natural appearance of the figures, since their light color more closely approximates reality. Moreover, details can be rendered much more naturally, in thick glaze called "relief line" and in a thinner glaze called "dilute glaze." This allows more natural, flowing lines than the incision used in the black-figure technique provides. No. 20 is a transition piece, using black-figure on the exterior and red-figure on the interior. No. 5 is an excellent example of the mature red-figure technique.

After the introduction of the red-figure technique, black-figure pottery continued to be produced until the mid-fifth century B.C., although its artistic merits were far below those of red-figure. No. 25 is an example of a debased black-figure product.

White-Ground

Contemporary with the production of red-figure pottery, the white-ground technique appeared. Potters covered the clay with a thick white slip on which figures were rendered in dark glaze, with details often in polychrome paint. In this delicate technique, Greek vase-painting achieved its closest proximity to monumental wall-painting, very little of which is preserved from Classical Greece. Joslyn's Nos. 27 and 28 are funerary lekythoi which are examples of the white-ground technique.

Fourth Century: 400–323 B.C.

Black-Glaze

Athenian production of red-figure pottery continued into the fourth century B.C. During the second quarter of the fifth century B.C., plain black pottery such as Nos. 32 and 33 appeared in large quantity. By the fourth century, this was the primary product of Athenian potters. Attic black-glaze pottery had numerous imitators; prominent among these were the South Italians, who produced such pieces as Nos. 35 and 36.

South Italian

Greek culture spread widely beginning in the eighth century B.C., as Greeks colonized to ease population pressure. Magna Graecia, as the Romans called Western Greece, was thus settled by colonies from mainland Greek states; the western territories developed similar but independent traditions in art, architecture, and intellectual pursuit, all grounded in mainstream Greek trends.

During the Archaic and early part of the Classical periods, the Greeks of South Italy, like the non-Greek Etruscans to the

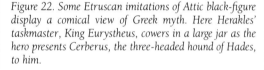

Figure 22. Some Etruscan imitations of Attic black-figure display a comical view of Greek myth. Here Herakles' taskmaster, King Eurystheus, cowers in a large jar as the hero presents Cerberus, the three-headed hound of Hades, to him.

north, imported figural pottery from Athens; like the Etruscans, too, they had independent local productions, some of which imitated mainland Greek pottery. During the third quarter of the fifth century B.C. the South Italians began to produce their own red-figure pottery. It is hypothesized that immigrant craftsmen from Athens, settled by the Athenian general Perikles at Thurii, were responsible for the red-figure production.

Although basically derivative, South Italian red-figure developed its own character and several regional styles emerged. Those represented in the Joslyn collection, Nos. 6 and 37–39, are from the area called Apulia. All productions range greatly in technical competence: some are on a par with the best Attic products; many are below it. Essentially, the dawn of the South Italian production came at the sunset of the red-figure technique. As a whole, South Italian productions were a lower quality postscript to the major Classical productions of ancient Athens.

Generally, South Italian vases are gaudy, with liberal use of added color. The quality of clay and glaze varies; frequently a thin red wash was applied to reserved areas to heighten the color of the clay.

Most shapes came from the Attic repertory but developed in idiosyncratic ways. Frequently decoration consists of trivial subjects such as we see on the pieces in the Joslyn collection: scenes of the boudoir and scenes of Eros. Both of these subjects also became popular on Athenian vases toward middle of the fifth century B.C. Often compositions contain incongruous elements, suggesting that artists aimed for a particular visual effect rather than a coherent narrative. It is often impossible to identify objects in the field, and particular combinations seem capricious.

Typically South Italian vases are "one-sided": there is one side which was clearly the most important and to which the most care was devoted. The other usually preserves perfunctory scenes of youths standing in conversation.

Overall, the testimony of the vases reiterates that Magna Graecia was an independent sphere of Greek culture, with its own tastes and traditions.

By the Hellenistic period, painted figural pottery was rarely produced; it was replaced by relief wares and black-glaze pottery decorated with floral ornament, as Nos. 40 and 41.

CATALOGUE

Catalogue

In general, the arrangement of vases in the exhibition is chronological. However, the first six vases have been extracted from their proper sequence to provide an initial orientation to the development of Greek pottery for visitors to the exhibition. A reference at the end of the entry indicates the other vases to which each of the initial vases relates.

1. Mycenaean Stirrup Jar

1960.265

Gift of the Joslyn Women's Association, 1960
Height, 0.292 m.; diameter, 0.266 m.
About 1150 B.C.
A and B: Octopus.

This shape derives its name from the arrangement of the handle: a false spout supports the two parts of the handle which resembles a stirrup. Liquids stored in the jar were poured through the narrow, easily sealed spout. The stirrup jar was created in Crete in the sixteenth century B.C. and became very popular throughout the Aegean from the fifteenth century onward. It was used for storage and transport.

During the Bronze Age the Greeks had no written history, so the archaeologist must rely especially on material remains such as pottery to reconstruct the historical record. The decoration of this piece reflects a great deal about the commercial and political situation in the Aegean at the end of the Bronze Age. Before 1450 B.C. the inhabitants of Crete, called Minoans after the legendary King Minos, were strong commercial and political forces in the Aegean. The Minoans created the stirrup jar for storage and export of commodities. They derived their artistic repertory from the natural world, showing particular affinity for acquatic subjects such as the octopus.

The mainlanders, called Mycenaeans after one of the principal seats of power, Mycenae, seem to have conquered Crete at about 1450 B.C., and they took over many Minoan artistic practices such as the production of stirrup jars with octopi as well. Under Mycenaean influence, the Minoan motifs became more formal and stylized, looking less and less like their natural models. Note on the Joslyn example that the body of the octopus is symmetrically disposed with respect to the vessel; there are geometric motifs on the shoulder which once may have represented other elements of the natural world.

During the twelfth century B.C. Mycenaean pottery was made both on the mainland and elsewhere, where the Mycenaeans had founded colonies or trading posts. The Joslyn example may have been made on the island of Naxos, although it was said to have been found in Rhodes.

By the time of the manufacture of the Joslyn piece, trade and communication in the Mycenaean world was threatened by waves of destructions brought about by conflicts in the Near East and the attacks of an enigmatic group called the "Peoples of the Sea." Pottery remained one of the few expressions of culture, and its nature and distribution tell us much about the historical situation.

The tendencies toward abstraction and geometric design which can be observed on the Joslyn piece are the distant progenitors of the Geometric style, which began in the tenth century B.C.

2. Attic Geometric Tankard

1963.479

Museum Purchase, 1963
Height to rim, 0.191 m.; diameter, 0.124 m.
750–725 B.C.
Three rectangular panels: bird, quadruped, bird.

The tankard probably served as a drinking and pouring vessel although its function is not certainly known. This example was produced in Athens, one of the most important centers of production of Geometric pottery.

As the name implies, the Geometric style relies on linear motifs which serve to define the structure of the vessel. Note how the neck is emphasized and set off both by the decorative panels and the lines which bound them. In this sense,

the principles of decoration are like those seen on the Mycenaean stirrup jar, No. 1; because of the affinity in approach to decorating pottery, scholars maintain that pottery production continued uninterrupted throughout the period of the Dark Ages. Also typical of the Geometric style is the tendency to fill the entire surface of the vase and the use of small floral ornaments to fill blank space in the panels with figural decoration.

Figures are drawn sparsely, in silhouette. Birds and deer entered the Attic repertory at about 850 B.C., along with other animals, but are subjected to the rigid Geometric style: note that the thighs and feet of the bird are reduced to triangles. This style is not realistic, but abstract. See No. 8.

3. Corinthian Alabastron

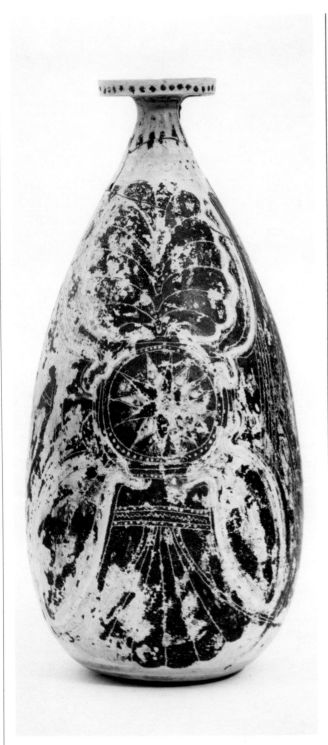

The alabastron, an oil container, was also a popular shape in the sixth century. Large examples, such as this one, were common by around 600 B.C.

Originally alabastra were decorated with friezes, but eventually Corinthian artists conceived of the entire shape as a single field and arranged the decoration symmetrically in terms of the whole. Note the similarity between the lotus-palmette cross on this piece and that on No. 10. See Nos. 9–12.

1961.559

Museum Purchase, 1961
Height, 0.270 m.; diameter, 0.131 m.
About 600–575 B.C.
Attributed to the Luxus Group.

4. Attic Black-Figure Hydria

44.1953

On permanent loan from the Anthropology Division,
   University of Nebraska State Museum
Formerly in the collection of George W. Lininger, Omaha
Height, 0.370 m.; width, including handles, 0.380 m.
Attributed to the Antimenes Painter. About 530–510 B.C.
Shoulder: A man mounts a four-horse chariot.
Body: Men harness a chariot.

The function of the hydria is discussed below with No. 17. This is the standard shape for a late sixth century B.C. black-figure hydria, with a flat shoulder and tapering body.

Scenes of harnessing are very common in Greek vase-painting; they are introduced into the repertory in the generation of painters which preceded the Antimenes Painter. Because chariots were no longer used in warfare in the sixth century B.C., we presume that both scenes on the Joslyn piece represent preparations for a procession or an athletic competition. However, because none of the figures is iden-tified by inscription, we cannot be certain whether this is a mythological event or a genre scene.

The Antimenes Painter is a close associate of the earliest red-figure painters. He experimented with the white-ground technique but for the most part stayed with the conservative black-figure.

Of the nearly 175 pieces attributed to the Antimenes Painter, six others preserve apparently non-mythological harnessing scenes. Although all use the same formula as seen on the Omaha piece, none is an exact repetition. The Omaha piece is distinct in that it shows an interest in creating a contrast between aged and youthful figures and an alternation between moving and stationary men. Moreover, we see an interest in the creation of depth: note that there are five superimposed planes in the scene. Although he is a conservative painter, the Antimenes Painter clearly likes to vary his vocabulary in several repetitions of the same syntax. See Nos. 15–25.

5. Attic Red-Figure Nolan Amphora

1965.407

Gift of Dr. J. Hewitt Judd, 1965
Height, 0.326 m.; diameter, 0.171 m.
Unattributed. About 450 B.C.
A: A winged male chases a female.
B: A youth stands facing right.

Amphoras of this type are named after a site in Italy where they are found in great abundance. Exclusively a red-figure shape, they are tall, slim neck-amphoras. A central rib on the handles, as is present here, is common on later examples of the shape.

Although we can be certain that a mythological chase is shown here, the identities of the participants are less obvious. There are no inscriptions, so the attributes of the characters must serve to identify them for us. We have few parallels for beardless, winged males who chase women. Ordinarily Eros, the personification of erotic love and the assistant of Aphrodite, is winged, but nude. Boreas, the north wind, is bearded. Hermes has a traveling hat, winged shoes, and a special staff. Here we must conclude either that the artist is depicting a figure unknown to us from the literary tradition, which is always a possibility, or that he was careless in his presentation of the scene. The bystander on the reverse is perfunctory and plays no significant part in the story.

Chase scenes are common in fifth century B.C. vase-painting, as part of a general interest, found prominently in literature and myth, in the violent aspects of erotic love. Here, a youth chases a woman; in many cases, the sexes are reversed. In myth and art such violent attacks are often metaphors for marriage. The Greek marriage ritual itself took the form of a mock kidnapping.

The chase and subsequent rape also stands as a metaphor for death: when an immortal kidnaps a mortal, taking him or her out of this world, the mortal dies. At least one ancient writer hypothesized that such myths originated as explanations for untimely, particularly premature, deaths. (Heraclitus C. 68). See Nos. 25; 28–30.

Figure 23. Here a mature Wind, perhaps Boreas—identified by his beard, wings, and winged shoes–, pursues a hapless woman.

6. Apulian Red-Figure Pelike

5.1984

On Permanent Loan from the Anthropology Division,
   University of Nebraska State Museum
Formerly in the collection of George W. Lininger, Omaha
Height, 0.275 m.; diameter, 0.187 m.
Attributed to the Dijon Painter. About 370 B.C.
A. A youth extends a bowl to a woman.
B. Two youths converse.

The pelike is a shape developed by Attic potters; it is actually a one-piece amphora with a low, broad belly. Note that unlike earlier amphoras, here the diameter of the mouth has grown so that it is almost as wide as the belly. As is the case with red-figure amphoras, pelikes would have been used as decanters.

The decoration on this piece reveals no specific mythological content; rather these are genre scenes. On A the context is benignly amorous, as a youth offers a bowl of fruit to a woman. The "quartered disc" above and the floral ornament below are simply decorative here and play no thematic role in the scene. On B the youths conversing are standard (see No. 37) and have no narrative meaning.

The rather careless and apparently hasty drawing on this piece is typical of much South Italian vase-painting. Compare, however, No. 37, which is of much higher quality. See Nos. 37–39.

7. Cypriot Amphora

1955.264

Museum Purchase, 1955
Height 0.225 m.; diameter, 0.260 m.
800–700 B.C.

Note the very general similarities in the basic shape of the Cypriot amphora to the Attic black- and red-figure examples, such as Nos. 5 and 16.

Horizontal bands together with circular elements in red, dark brown, or black paint are characteristic of Cypriot pottery; just as with Greek Geometric, linear elements emphasize the various parts of the vessel.

This amphora demonstrates that the affinities of Greek pottery reach to the east as well as to the west: there are intermittent connections between Greek and Cypriot pottery which begin in the Mycenaean period and continue through the Archaic period.

8. East Greek Geometric Bird Bowl

1967.9

Museum Purchase, 1967
Height, 0.040 m.; diameter of rim, 0.092 m.
675-640 B.C.
Central rectangular panel: bird in silhouette.

This bowl is a small drinking vessel; it was produced by Greeks living in Asia Minor, called East Greece or Ionia.

Although by 700 B.C. the Geometric style had died out for the most part and was replaced by Orientalizing styles, it lingered on in East Greece in the form and decoration of so-called "bird bowls." Note the similarity between the bird panels on the cup and those on the Geometric tankard, No. 2.

East Greece was an extremely important area in cultural terms for the Greeks, from the Geometric period onward. It was a region through which many Oriental influences passed through to Greece proper, and it was very prominent as an intellectual center. The bird bowl is a good example of how Ionia shared a great deal with the mainland but had its own distinctive traditions.

9-11. Corinthian Aryballoi

The round aryballos, developed in Corinth at the end of the seventh century B.C., was used as a container for precious oils. The wide flat lip and small mouth are specially designed to limit the amount which could be poured from the vessel.

Aryballoi such as these three Joslyn examples tell a great deal about the historical picture and the commercial prominence of Corinth. The number of these small oil containers found in Greece and in the east and west are estimated to be in the tens of thousands. The floral ornaments which appear are ultimately derived from the Near East, as the shape itself may well be. The appearance of these Near Eastern motifs on Greek pottery illustrates the enormous influence which the Near East had on Greece during this period.

1948.118.5

Gift of the Honorable Hugh H. Butler, 1948
Height, 0.058 m.; diameter, 0.055 m.
About 575-550 B.C.
Marching foot soldiers.

It is not clear whether this is a contemporary scene or one from myth; we do know that during the sixth century the development of military strategy involving phalanxes of foot soldiers carrying round shields occurred.

1948.118.4

Gift of the Honorable Hugh H. Butler, 1948
Height, 0.060 m.; diameter, 0.064 m.
About 600 B.C.

Most of the decoration on this aryballos is floral: there is a rosette on the top of the mouth, and a quadruple lotus with cross-hatched calyxes covers much of the body.

1954.3

Gift of Mrs. A. F. Jonas, 1954
Height, 0.063 m.; diameter, 0.060 m.
About 600-575 B.C.

This aryballos also relies on florals for the primary decoration: here, petals decorate the top of the mouth, and a cross combining lotus and palmette covers much of the body. In this example, the black-figure technique includes incision for detail and added red for a polychromous effect.

12. Corinthian Amphoriskos

1963.483

Museum Purchase, 1963
Height, 0.160 m.; diameter, 0.100 m.
Close to the Ampersand Painter. About 600-575 B.C.
Two horizontal zones of animal frieze.

The amphoriskos, or small amphora, was used for the storage or transport of liquids. It was a popular shape in the Middle Corinthian period. Compare the Corinthian type to Attic versions such as No. 21.

The black-figure animal frieze is the most characteristic scheme of decoration on Corinthian pottery. As with the floral ornaments, the repertory of animal figures is largely taken over from the Near East. Some of the animals, such as grazing deer and birds, could have been drawn from the artists' own observations; others, such as panthers and lions, would have been very rare in Greece, if they were present at all. By the time of manufacture of the Joslyn amphoriskos, animal frieze pieces were mass-produced. Note how elongated the bodies of animals are and how extensive and crude the filling ornaments.

13. Italo-Corinthian Olpe

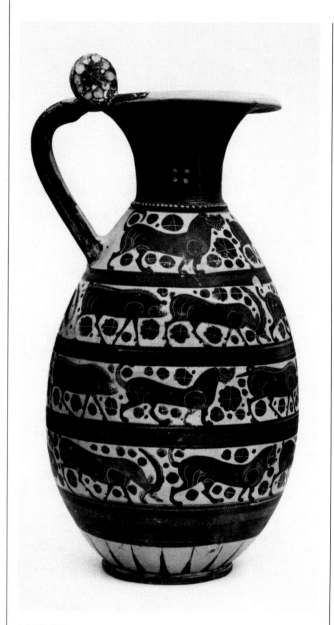

The olpe was a shape invented by the Corinthians and frequently imitated by the Etruscans, as this example indicates. It was used as a pitcher, to pour liquids.

Italo-Corinthian pottery, as such copies as these are called, was produced in Etruria beginning at about 600 B.C.; these copies give testimony to the enormous popularity of Corinthian pottery in the west. The closeness to Corinthian models varies; comparison to animal friezes on No. 12 illustrates original and copy: panthers on the Corinthian amphora are in proper proportion with the exception of the elongated bodies. Those on the Etruscan copies have extraordinarily short legs and small heads. Note also the extremely exaggerated horns on the Etruscan goats.

1963.478

Museum Purchase, 1963
Height, 0.389 m.; diameter, 0.195 m.
Attributed to the Joslyn Painter. About 580 B.C.
Four horizontal zones of animal frieze.

14. Bucchero Oinochoe

Etruscan bucchero or "grey ware" is one of the few types of fine ancient pottery which is unpainted. The clay is very highly refined and fired a dark grey with a glossy black finish. In its earliest phases shapes are elegant and preserve elaborate incised and impressed decoration; in the sixth century B.C. bucchero becomes much more heavy and clumsy, as the Joslyn example.

The shape, with trefoil mouth, is specifically designed for pouring. Like No. 13 it follows a Corinthian model: note that both have "ears" which are attached on the rim near the handle.

Decoration on this oinochoe, a wine-pouring vessel, is typical of the later, more clumsy phase of bucchero produced at or near the site of Chiusi: it consists of thin bands in raised relief, incised zigzags on the neck, impressed petals on the shoulder, and impressed rosettes on the "ears."

Bucchero of this type was made at several Etruscan sites and was not widely exported.

1965.278

Gift of Horace Morison, 1965
Height, 0.373 m.; diameter, 0.173 m.
About 550-500 B.C.

15. Attic Black-Figure Komast Cup

1951.885

Museum Purchase, 1951
Height, 0.080 m. (without foot); diameter of rim, 0.201 m.
Attributed to the Falmouth Painter. About 590-570 B.C.
Six padded dancers.

Komast cups are drinking vessels which derive their name from the lively figures which decorate them. These cups or kylikes are among the earliest black-figure cups to have been produced in Attica. Several features of this cup illustrate the strong influence which Corinthian painters had on early Attic black-figure. Attic shapes are copied directly, although they are slightly lighter than their models. The figures who dance on the Joslyn cup are also copied from the Corinthians, as are the subsidiary floral motifs, such as rosettes; the latter can be seen on a number of the Corinthian examples in the Joslyn collection.

The dancers are a special class of entertainers who wore artificially padded bellies and thighs to increase comic effect. From the representations it appears that the dances were lively and involved exaggerated movements and much slapping of thighs and buttocks. Usually the dancers are male, as seen here, but they may be accompanied by female companions as well. Komast scenes are among our earliest examples of depictions of contemporary life in Greek vase-painting.

16. Attic Black-Figure Ovoid Neck-Amphora

1963.480

Gift of Mr. and Mrs. Thomas C. Woods, Jr., 1963
Height, 0.359 m.; diameter, 0.237 m.
Attributed to the Omaha Painter. About 570 B.C.

A: Greek warrior fighting an Amazon with three spectators on each side.
B: Symposium of three reclining banqueters paired with female companions.

The amphora is one of the most common shapes in the Greek pottery repertory. The name means literally "carried on both sides" and refers to the two handles. The piece is a neck-amphora because the neck is sharply set off from the body. It is part of a class called "Tyrrhenian" by scholars, because these amphoras were almost exclusively exported to the Etruscans, whom the Greeks called "Tyrrhenoi." This amphora was probably used to hold liquids as a decanter.

The characteristic features of the Tyrrhenian class include the use of color and the use of animal friezes and florals in the lower zones of decoration.

Apparently we have a combination of mythological and genre scenes here. Side A shows a Greek hero slaying an Amazon; this is the earliest example in our collection to illustrate one of the most popular Greek myths. Amazons were a mythical race of barbarian women who were thought to live to the north, at the edge of the world known to the Greeks. They fought as men, and often, in art, only the color of their flesh distinguishes them from male warriors.

According to Greek myth, Amazons fought against Greek heroes on several occasions. In addition to Herakles' campaign against them to obtain the belt of the Amazon queen, the Amazons were said to have come to Athens itself and were defeated there by the hero Theseus. The Greeks regarded the latter victory as one of the great triumphs of their civilization over that of barbarians and used it later as a mythical comparison to their actual victory over the Persians. Greeks set themselves apart from all other races, recognizing that their culture, way of government, and particularly their language differed significantly from other groups. For this reason, the Greeks liked to show themselves as conquering barbarians in art, as it demonstrated the superiority of their culture.

Side B shows an event presumably dealing with ordinary mortals. The symposium was an all-male dinner and drinking party which might be attended, as seen here, by hired *hetairai* or "female companions." Respectable women did not come into contact with men outside of the home and would never be present at a symposium. Note that ancient eating customs differed from ours. Greeks reclined on couches and reached to smaller tables in front of the couches for their food. They were served wine by young boys and drank it out of kylikes or cups such as No. 15. From architectural evidence, we know that the dining couches were arranged in a square, around the walls of the dining room. Such dining rooms were called *androns* or "men's rooms" because they were used exclusively by the men in the family.

Dogs waiting for scraps are often part of the scene. Although they were not really pets as we know them, dogs were important to hunters and generated strong feelings on the part of their owners.

Dr. Dietrich von Bothmer of The Metropolitan Museum of Art identified this painter and fittingly nicknamed him "the Omaha Painter." Only one other piece is attributed to our painter. It is in the Louvre and shows the birth of Athena from the head of Zeus, and musicians.

Certain conventions of Attic black-figure technique can be observed on this piece: added white is used for women's flesh to indicate that they were very rarely exposed to the sun, unlike men, who moved about outside freely.

The production of this class of vases, of which we have more than 200 preserved, illustrates the responsiveness of the Attic potter to commercial opportunity. The Corinthians had previously controlled Etruscan markets; the Athenians used Corinthian schemes of color and decoration, to which the Etruscan clientele had become accustomed, to make their shape and product more successful. The primary "Corinthianizing" elements are the lavish use of added white and red and the animal frieze. The Tyrrhenian class is consciously old-fashioned then in subject matter as well as decorative scheme, for by the end of the second quarter of the sixth century B.C., most Attic potters had moved away from Corinthian fashions.

Figure 24. The Louvre amphora by the Omaha Painter depicts the birth of Athena from the head of Zeus.

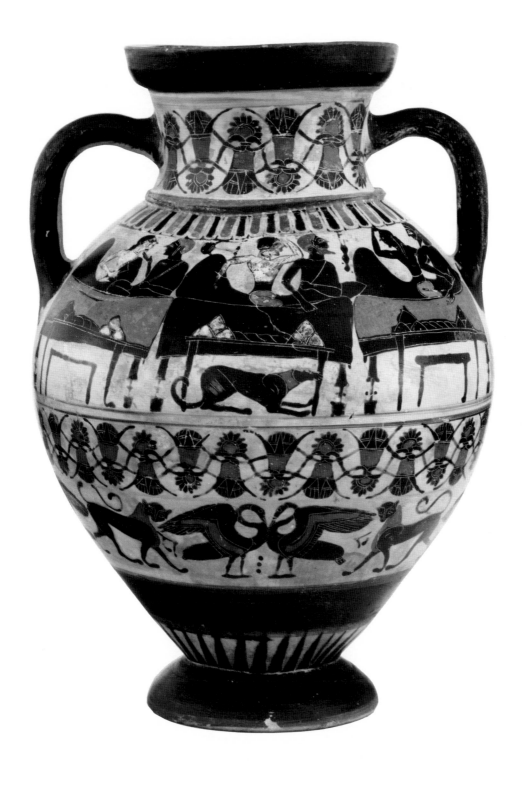

17. Attic Black-Figure Hydria

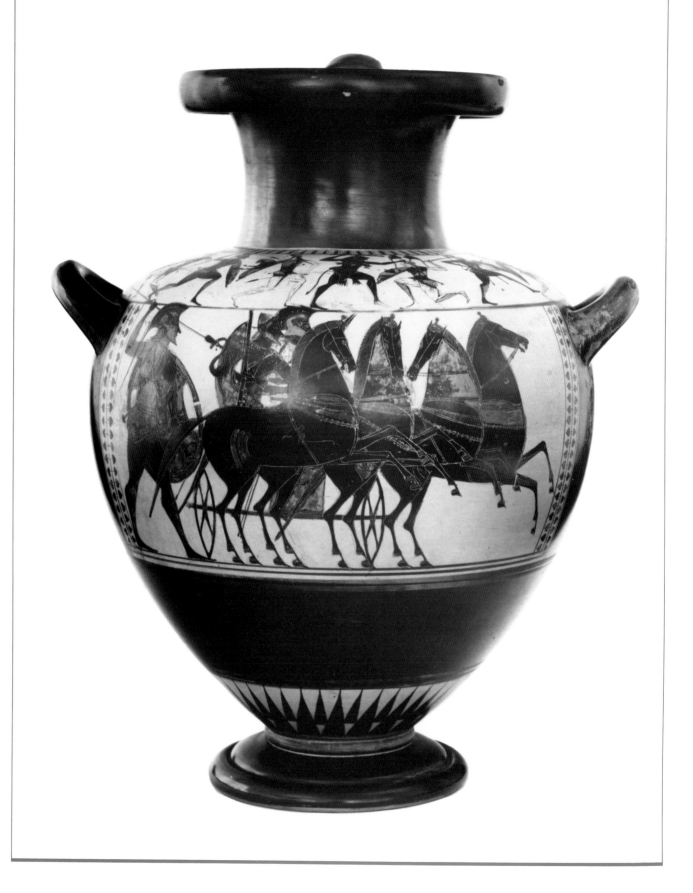

1953.255

Museum Purchase, 1953
Height, 0.415 m.; diameter, 0.303 m.
Attributed to the Affecter. About 530 B.C.
Shoulder: Herakles and Greek heroes in battle with the
    Amazons.
Body: Warriors and charioteer with chariot wheeling
    round.

The term "hydria" comes from the Greek word for water, *hudor,* and suggests the function of the piece: to hold and carry water. The two horizontal handles at shoulder level are used for lifting and the vertical handle for pouring. There are numerous representations on Attic vases which show Athenian women at public fountains filling hydrias. As is the case with many shapes of Attic vases, there is a close relationship between this shape and metal vessels; evidence of this are the imitation rivets on the inside of the mouth.

This example is an extremely rare type of hydria. It differs from the standard type in many respects, all of which suggest that it is a bit old-fashioned for the period in which the painter worked: the low pouring handle, low, broad neck, and rounded shoulder differ from most contemporary hydrias, of which the fragmentary No. 4 is a good example.

The Affecter is also old-fashioned in his decorative schemes: note the way in which the shoulder panel extends beyond the main panel. As his name suggests, he is an "affected" artist, part of a group called "Mannerist." This group deliberately seeks to be old-fashioned in a period when the black-figure technique is just past its prime. The mannered, angular poses and elongated proportions of his figures, with small heads and long limbs, exhibit this tendency. Their poses have been compared to those of marionettes.

The Affecter painted over 100 pieces; of these, only two others are hydrias. Most of his subject matter is trivial; this piece is unusually substantial in theme. His attention to detail and love of intricacy is remarkable; note how he varies the details of what each figure wears. His vividness can be seen in the abundance of added color and his liveliness in the elaborate, vital shield decorations. Note particularly the human face which forms part of the decorative pattern on

the long white garment of the charioteer.

The Amazonomachy, or "fight with Amazons," seen on the shoulder is the same theme which appears on No. 16. Here, however, the hero Herakles is spotlighted as he duels with an Amazon. Although there is no inscription, we can identify Herakles by his attributes, the lionskin and club. One of Herakles' Twelve Labors, assigned by King Eurystheus of Tiryns, was to bring back the belt of the Amazon queen; when in a general battle context, it is difficult to tell whether the labor is intended or a generic fight with Amazons. We can see that this is a battle of older heroes, however, because they use primitive weapons, such as clubs, and some of them wear animal skins, a primitive form of armour.

We also know that the battle scene on the main panel is not contemporary, but must be heroic as well. By the sixth century, Greeks no longer fought from chariots. Only mythological heroes, such as those described by Homer, actually fight from chariots. This point is discussed further with No. 4.

However, the variety of arms and armour as seen here does give some evidence of what was actually used by the Greeks of the Archaic period. Greeks certainly did not fight with bare feet and vast expanses of naked flesh exposed, nor did they wear animal skins or carry clubs as standard weapons. These are aspects of "heroic license." However, archaeologists have uncovered round shields, both of leather and metal, corselets or cuirasses, swords and spearheads, greaves, and both Attic and Corinthian type helmets. The latter type is distinguished by the fact that it covers the entire face. So, although it must be used with caution, evidence of arms and armour on vases such as this can be used to supplement and corroborate the often poorly preserved material evidence and, therefore, to enlarge our knowledge of ancient warfare. The same holds true for the rich decoration of the figures' garments. Cloth from antiquity rarely survives, so we must look to representations on vases to gain an impression of it.

On the underside of the piece there are two scratched letters, *alpha* and *rho.* Such marks appear often on vases and probably serve either as a price, an indication of destination, or the point of origin of the piece.

Figure 25. The hero Theseus also encountered Amazons. Here he abducts their Queen, Antiope.

18. Attic Black-Figure Band-Cup

1966.56

Museum Purchase, 1966
Height, 0.140 m.; diameter of rim, 0.206 m.
Unattributed. About 540–530 B.C.
Animal frieze: Deer grazing between Sirens between panthers.

Figure 26. Odysseus resists the beguiling song of the Sirens only because he had instructed his crew to tie him to the ship's mast.

This type of cup, a Little Master cup, is a descendant of the Komast cup, No. 15. Note that the bowl is shallower and the handles are placed lower. Little Master cups derive their name from the miniaturist drawing style used to decorate them. This is a "band-cup" because the decorated area is a reserved band going around the piece at the handle zone.

The animal frieze which decorates this piece has its ultimate origins in the Corinthian repertory, as No. 12, where the panthers appear as well. Sirens, which appear here, are hybrid creatures like sphinxes: they combine a female head with the body of a bird.

Sirens have an ambiguous role in Greek mythology. Homer, in the *Odyssey*, informs us that Sirens live on an island near Scylla and Charybdis, and sailors, charmed by their song, land there and perish. Odysseus follows the advice of Circe and passes safely by them. It is not certain exactly what Sirens represent to the Greek psyche; their persistent association with death is certain. Originally, they may have been perceived as birds inhabited by the souls of the dead; by the Archaic period, they accompany the dead on their voyage to the lower world and are frequently seen crowning stone tomb monuments. In this example, however, their context is decorative rather than mythological.

19. Attic Black-Figure Kyathos

1963.484

Museum Purchase, 1963
Height to top of handle spur, 0.163 m.; diameter of rim,
    0.120 m.
Attributed as "related to the Theseus Painter." About
    515–500 B.C.
Dionysos mounts a chariot accompanied by five figures,
    including Hermes and Nike.

The kyathos is a dipper used to ladle wine from a krater
to a cup for drinking. This shape, like No. 16, is an excellent
example of the way in which Attic potters developed their
product for particular markets. In the case of the kyathos,
potters copied a shape in the local repertory of the Etruscans.

On this kyathos we see an especially fine rendering of a
Dionysiac scene; here the god mounts a chariot with his
retinue, perhaps on his way to Olympus. The messenger
divinity, Hermes, guides him. Here, in contrast to the presentation on No. 21, the maenads are quite sedate and the
procession includes satyrs. These mythical male followers of
Dionysos are distinguished by their shaggy beards and hair,
long pointed ears, and tails; here they are chubby as well.
Satyrs are lewd and wild when possessed with the ecstatic
spirit of the god. For a discussion of the mythological background of this scene and the worship of the god, see No. 21.

20. Attic Black-Figure Type A Cup

1957.5

Jasper Hall Memorial Fund Purchase, 1957
Height, 0.070 m.; diameter of rim with handles,
0.269 m.
Attributed to the Group of Cambridge 62. About 525–515
    B.C.
Interior: Gorgoneion.
A and B: Dionysos seated, between eyes.

The Type A cup is a further descendant of the Komast
cup and the Little Master cup. Note how the foot becomes
increasingly shorter and the bowl increasingly more flat.
This type of cup is characterized by the appearance of eyes
on the exterior, the meaning of which is not clear. They may
ward off evil, in the same way that the "evil eye" functions
today in modern Turkey. Another suggestion is that the eyes
are humorous: in profile the cup looks like a face with two
ears; the addition of the eyes makes it seem even more like
a face. To find man in almost any form reflects a characteristically Greek outlook.

Here the magical relationship between Dionysos and the
vine is stressed, as the god holds the vine in the same hand
with his drinking horn or rhyton. This is a case where
function and decoration are intertwined: one drinks wine
from a cup which depicts the god of wine. In the interior is
the decapitated head of the Gorgon, called a "Gorgoneion";
this frightening apparition was used by the Archaic Greeks
as a means to ward off evil. Note that the interior is rendered
in the red-figure technique, while the exterior is in black-
figure. Such combinations of technique are not unusual during the period when red-figure was being introduced.

21. Attic Black-Figure Neck-Amphora

1965.408

Gift of Dr. and Mrs. J. Hewitt Judd, 1965
Height, 0.257 m.; diameter, 0.173 m.
Unattributed. About 500 B.C.
A: Dionysos rides an ithyphallic mule flanked by dancing
  maenads.
B: Departure of warriors.

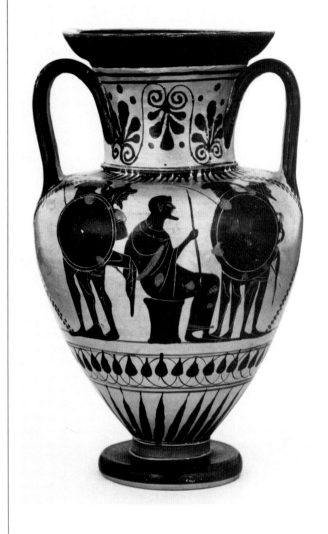

The amphora is a tremendously popular shape in the black-figure workshops of the late sixth century B.C.

Dionysos, seen on A, was one of the primary fertility deities for the agriculturally-oriented Greeks. He was specifically identified as the patron of the vine and its cultivated product, wine. Celebration of the Dionysiac cult was of major importance to the Greeks, and it had a tremendous popular following. One of the most prominent literary sources which we have for the features of the cult of Dionysos is Euripides' tragedy, the *Bacchae*; we are able to corroborate elements of both myth and cult from the evidence of vases such as this example. Both because of his general popularity and because it was natural to decorate vessels used for wine with episodes from the life of its patron, Dionysiac scenes are of the most common to appear on Attic vases.

Dionysos is identified by his beard, leafy wreath, and the drinking vessel which he often carries; here it is a rhyton, as on No. 20. He rides a mule, so this scene may be an excerpt from those where the god enters Mount Olympus with the god Hephaistos. As is usual, Dionysos himself is quite placid, but his female followers dance enthusiastically, filled with the ecstatic power of the god. These female followers are called "maenads"; their name is from the same root as the English word "mania." Maenads, in myth, are mortal women who undergo dramatic transformations under the influence of the god. In his tragedy, the *Bacchae*, Euripides gives an account of their behavior, as they nurse wild beasts and rend them limb from limb. Although the worship of Dionysos did not include such acts, there is evidence for cults of maenads in various parts of Greece. Wild behavior was certainly part of cult celebration. In cultural terms the worship of Dionysos provided a means for the populace to indulge in behavior normally forbidden in a way that was not disruptive to society.

Side B is a military scene. We see a moment of leave-taking, where youthful warriors are bidding farewell to an elderly gentleman. The archers, identified in part by their shaggy beards and soft leather caps, who appear here are part of a special class of mercenaries who may have acted as policemen in the city of Athens. They are from the area that is now South Russia, called Scythia in antiquity. Scythian archers were one of many groups of foreigners who lived in Athens. They were not citizens proper but had the rights and privileges of free men. The vase-painter gives them a shaggy appearance to stress their non-Greek origins.

22. Attic Black-Figure Column-Krater

1965.166

Gift of Mr. and Mrs. Thomas C. Woods, Jr., 1965
Height, 0.357 m.; diameter, 0.313 m.
Unattributed. About 520–500 B.C.
A: Chariot with four horses, driver, and warrior.
B: Warrior and groom depart.

The column-krater is a large vessel used for mixing wine; Greeks drank wine heavily diluted with water, and this fact helps to explain why both containers and cups had such a large capacity. One would use a kyathos, as No. 19, to dip wine out of the krater and then pour it into a cup such as No. 20 for drinking. Kraters, kyathoi, and kylikes would be important pieces of table ware at symposia such as that depicted on No. 16.

The history of this shape again shows the important inspiration which Attic potters derived from the Corinthians. Originally a Corinthian shape, this type of krater entered the Attic repertory in the early sixth century B.C.; it derives its modern name from the appearance of the double vertical handles, which look very much like columns supporting the rectangular handle plates.

Military themes prevail on this krater. Side A probably has a heroic reference, since the readied chariot is presumably that of the armed warrior. As explained in the discussion of No. 4, Greeks of the Archaic and Classical periods no longer fought from chariots. If the figure does go to fight, he will attack his enemy from the chariot while his charioteer skillfully maneuvers.

Side B depicts a warrior's leave-taking. As the warrior leaves, his squire, who tends his horse, says a final farewell to the figure at the right. Although different in detail, the message here is very similar to that on No. 29.

23. Attic Black-Figure Neck-Amphora

98.1968

Lent in memory of Barbara Y. Merrill
Height, 0.140 m.; diameter, 0.089 m.
Unattributed. About 500 B.C.
Two identical trios of two youths with a winged female
    form a continuous figural zone.

This is a small amphora, very similar in shape to its larger counterparts such as Nos. 4 and 21. Presumably household needs or the sale of a particular commodity dictated the necessity for the production of smaller versions of standard shapes.

The chase scene does not have reference to a specific myth. Its repetition on both sides of the piece suggests a rather thoughtless and cursory approach on the part of the artist. Such hastiness is common among black-figure artists of the late sixth century. The winged female figure may be Nike, the personification of victory, or Iris, the messenger goddess. The chase itself is a common theme: see No. 5. Here the animated poses and gestures lend excitement to the scene.

24. Attic Black-Figure Lekythos

1924.8

Gift of the Art Institute of Omaha, 1931
Height, 0.164 m.; diameter of shoulder, 0.064 m.
Unattributed. About 475–450 B.C.
A warrior mounts a chariot in the company of Athena; at
the right, a man at an altar.

The cylinder lekythos is the most common type of oil
container from the time of its invention in the last quarter
of the sixth century B.C. until nearly the end of the fifth
century. It is used in domestic contexts and appears very
frequently as a funeral gift as well. These lekythoi are the
relatives and descendants of the Corinthian aryballoi, Nos.
9–11. As with aryballoi, cylinder lekythoi are small; this
small size suggests that oil was used and transported in very
small quantities. The small mouth with flat lip helped to
control the amounts of the precious contents which were
poured.

The white-ground technique is used (see pages 36 and
70) here with black-figure. Note the actual color of the clay
which is visible on the side of the foot. Lekythoi are grouped
into workshops by analysis of subsidiary decoration and
subtleties of shape, as well as figural style. The particular
arrangement of the shoulder palmettes and the placement of
the groups of berries helps to place this piece near the
workshop of the Beldam Painter, while the attitude of the
figures tells us that it is by a follower of the Pholos Painter.
While it cannot be assigned to a particular hand, by these
methods we can achieve some idea of its date and stylistic
affinities.

The presence of the goddess Athena, identified by her
helmet, shield, and spear, tells us that the scene itself is
certainly heroic, although we cannot determine its specific
reference. The shields which the artist uses in this scene,
distinctive because of the cut-outs on either side, were be-
loved by Athenian artists; apparently they were never actually used in combat. The altar in the scene suggests that
the warriors may be in the process of making an offering
before setting off for battle.

25. Attic Black-Figure Lekythos

This lekythos shows a very sketchy version of a banquet like the symposium seen on No. 16. Here one *hetaira*, or female companion, provides musical entertainment with a lyre. By comparing this lekythos with the earlier scene, it is obvious how standard scenes degenerated over the century which separates this example from No. 16.

1931.116

Bequest of Jessie Barton Christiancy, 1931
Height, 0.120 m.; diameter of shoulder, 0.045 m.
Attributed to the Manner of the Haimon Painter. About
    475–450 B.C.
Male reclining on a banquet couch with female attendants.

26. Attic Red-Figure Lekythos

This red-figure lekythos is of nearly identical shape to No. 27, and it may well be by the same painter. Here, however, the function is probably not exclusively funerary, for the scene is one of generic domesticity, appropriate for a perfume container. The column tells us that the scene is indoors, as does the rather ambiguous piece of furniture and the piece of cloth which hangs on the wall.

The column which is shown here is of the Doric order and is probably partially or completely made of wood. In addition to the marble columns used in temples, ancient Greeks used wooden columns for much civic and domestic architecture. These columns made out of ephemeral materials no longer exist, and archaeologists sometimes turn to evidence such as the painting here to gain an impression of wooden architecture.

1954.2

Gift of Mrs. A. F. Jonas, 1954
Height, 0.158 m.; diameter of shoulder, 0.053 m.
Unattributed. About 475–450 B.C.
A woman stands in front of a Doric column.

White-Ground Lekythoi

Around the second quarter of the fifth century, Attic potters began to produce a special type of lekythos which was specifically intended for use in funerary ritual. We are certain of the function of these vessels because they are found almost exclusively in graves, and the scenes painted on them often have to do with funerary subjects. Although we must exercise caution in their interpretation, these lekythoi give us a great deal of information about Athenian burial practice and about an unusual technique of Attic painting.

Characteristically, white-ground funerary lekythoi show scenes relating to an Athenian funeral; from them we learn how the Athenians went about mourning their loved ones. The aspect of funerary ritual which involved white-ground lekythoi must have been specifically Athenian, for we do not usually find that these vases were exported elsewhere. There are two exceptions to this: at Corinth and Eretria, both relatively near Athens, they were not only used in grave contexts, they were imitated as well. This suggests that the Corinthians and Eretrians may have had some special affinity with the Athenians in the area of funerary custom.

These lekythoi are decorated with polychrome matte paint against a thick white slip; the latter gives the technique its name. White-ground is a very delicate technique which could not have withstood the rigors of daily use. In general, white-ground pieces are thought to be the closest representatives which we have of monumental wall-painting of the fifth century. The color scheme and mode of depiction seem to have been very similar on both wall-painting and white-ground vases. Although literary sources testify that there were great examples of Classical wall-painting, virtually none of it is preserved today. Thanks to the evidence of white-ground lekythoi, we have some idea of how the monumental wall-paintings would have looked.

Figure 27. A fragmentary vessel preserves mourning women surrounding the corpse of a loved one.

27. Attic White-Ground Lekythos

1954.1

Gift of Mrs. A. F. Jonas, 1954
Height, 0.184 m.; diameter of shoulder, 0.065 m.
Attributed to the Tymbos Painter. About 475–450 B.C.
A woman places a wreath on a grave monument.

Here we see a woman adorning the marker which stood over the tomb of a loved one. Such markers could be elaborate; this one is fairly modest, although it was made of stone and was, therefore, expensive. It has a three-stepped base, a rectangular shaft, and a triangular crowning member called a "pediment." The pediment gives the monument the appearance of a building, and we know from later examples that the Greeks often perceived grave markers as small shrines. Some gravestones had sculptural decoration, although none is preserved on this example. The mourning woman here places a wreath on the grave marker; note that it is already decorated with sashes.

The Tymbos Painter is named after the mound or *tymbos* which often appears on his lekythoi; our example lacks such a mound.

28. Attic White-Ground Lekythos

1953.256

Museum Purchase, 1953
Height, 0.310 m.; diameter of shoulder, 0.090 m.
Attributed to the Dessypri Painter. About 450–425 B.C.
A woman stands in front of a chair, holding a wreath before her.

This white-ground lekythos shows a scene which does not specifically reflect activity at the tomb, despite the fact that it, like No. 27, probably served a funerary function. It is common for white-ground lekythoi to show domestic scenes just as it is common for such subjects to appear on carved stone grave markers. Presumably they simply show the deceased in a characteristic daily activity.

29. Attic Red-Figure Nolan Amphora

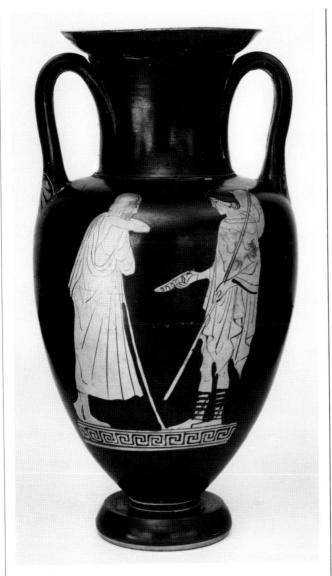

1957.6

Gift of the Joslyn Women's Association, 1957
Height, 0.345 m.; diameter, 0.176 m.
Attributed as "in the neighborhood of the Painter of
   London E 342." About 450 B.C.
A: A youth leaves home.
B: A youth faces left.

For a discussion of this shape, see No. 5.

On the main scene, we see a leave-taking of a slightly different type than that on No. 22. Here the discrepancy in age between the two figures is stressed, as is typical in the art of the Early Classical period. During this period, in the aftermath of the Persian Wars, Greeks began to analyze their experience in a different way and emphasized differences in states of being, such as extremes in age. The youth here wears a costume more suited for traveling or hunting than for battle. The phiale held by the youth is clearly drawn here: it is a bowl with a shallow body and a depression on the undersurface; the latter is useful for holding the handle-less vessel. Such bowls are most common in metal and the example here may have vertical petal ribbing. Phialai were used on ceremonial occasions to receive libations. Here a libation received by the youth would serve to give good luck to his adventure.

The single figure on the reverse is anonymous. The practice of spotlighting one or two figures on one side of a piece began at the end of the first decade of the fifth century. Anonymous figures such as the one here become very common by the second quarter of the fifth century B.C. and are particularly common on Nolan amphoras.

30. Attic Red-Figure Type B Cup

1953.257

Museum Purchase, 1953
Height, 0.085 m.; diameter of rim, 0.232 m.
Unattributed. About 460–440 B.C.
Interior: Eros presents a chest to a seated woman.
A and B: Identical courtship or marriage scenes appear on
   each side: Eros stands between a youth and a woman.

This shape is a type B kylix, and with it we see the final
development of the Attic cup as the sequence appears in the
Joslyn collection. The bowl is extremely broad and shallow.

The subject matter is repetitious and concerns courtship
or marriage. Eros, the servant of Aphrodite, brings a gift of
a chest to a woman alone and, on the exterior, to a youth
and a woman. The chest and its contents are love gifts or
wedding gifts. Eros is not their donor, but their conveyor.
Iconography such as this becomes very common by the second quarter and middle years of the fifth century B.C. Most
frequently it appears on shapes closely related to the activities of women.

As the subject matter on Greek pottery becomes less concerned with myth and more concerned with trivial scenes
such as this, it becomes less viable as an art form. By the
end of the fifth century there is very little serious subject
matter on Attic vases.

31. Attic Red-Figure Bell-Krater

1963.485

Gift of the Joslyn Women's Association, 1963
Height, 0.418 m.; diameter, 0.433 m.
Attributed to the Painter of Munich 2335. About 430–420
  B.C.
A: Herakles and Athena with Hera and Iris.
B: A jumper with Nike and a trainer.

This type of krater takes its name from the fact that when turned upside down, it looks very much like a bell. The bell-krater is a close relative of the column-krater, as No. 22. Such a large vessel as this would have served as a wine bowl; it may have been the centerpiece at the celebration of a victorious athlete, such as the jumper on B.

This is a case where the evidence preserved on pottery differs from that which we have in the literary tradition, because it presents an unusual twist in the combination of Herakles and Hera. The hero Herakles is clearly at the end of his labors on A: Iris has conducted him to Olympus, where Athena pours him a libation from her oinochoe, a pitcher, into his kantharos, a drinking cup. Hera waits in the background to make amends with her former enemy; although ironically, Herakles' name means "Glory of Hera," she hated the hero and caused him great hardship. Even though Herakles ultimately marries Hera's daughter, Hebe, Herakles and his mother-in-law are rarely shown together in art.

The association of the themes on the two sides of this piece may be deliberate, for Herakles served as a paradigm to athletic victors. He was founder of the Olympic Games as well as other Panhellenic, or "all-Greek" games. The victorious jumper on B is likened to Herakles, victorious in the completion of his labors, many of which required athletic skills to complete. Greek mortals loved Herakles because he represented a kind of hope of immortality; after a difficult life as only a demi-god, he, by painstaking effort, achieved a spot among the immortals. As discussed by Professor Beye above, the juxtaposition of athletes and athletic victory with Herakles and his labors is a theme reiterated in the literary record.

The athletic event shown on B is closest to our modern long jump. In the ancient event, however, the contestant held weights or *halteres* in his hands to improve his distance. The post probably represents the starting point of the event.

32. Attic Black-Glaze Skyphos

1962.209

Gift of Mrs. Wentworth Dodge, 1962
Height, 0.090 m.; diameter of rim, 0.110 m.
About 475–450 B.C.

Athenian pottery workshops produced very high quality pottery which was painted black and decorated with reserved areas but no painted figural decoration. In some cases, shapes in the black-glaze repertory are identical to those with figural decoration.

Attic black-glaze pottery was widely exported and imitated. The shapes suggest that it was used just as painted pottery, as table ware. Presumably it was a grade slightly below that of pottery with figural decoration. Large scale production of black-glaze pottery began in the mid-fifth century and continued through the fourth century B.C.

Artists who worked on black-glaze pottery are identified somewhat differently than on pottery with figural decoration. Patterns of decoration on the undersurface and types and arrangements of stamped decoration serve as the criteria for distinguishing workshops.

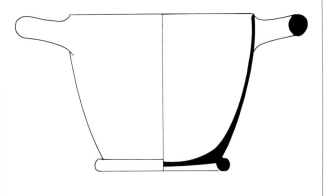

Figure 28. Profile of skyphos. Profile drawings, such as those illustrated here for Nos. 32–34, provide archaeologists with a means to objective analysis of shape.

This type of drinking vessel was created by Attic potters in the mid-sixth century B.C. Originally based on Corinthian models, the skyphos settled down to an independent, consistent shape by the early fifth century. The relatively early features of this piece include the single curve from foot to rim and widest possible diameter at the rim. The red wash in the reserved areas of this piece is commonly applied to heighten the color of the clay.

One of the most interesting features of this piece is the wax seal preserved at the center of the undersurface. This identifies the skyphos as having once belonged in the collection of the Bourbon family, the Royal House of the Two Sicilies. This family ruled over Sicily from 1735 until the time of Garibaldi in the 1860s.

33. Attic Black-Glaze Stemless Cup

1952.259

Gift of Dr. J. Hewitt Judd, 1952
Height, 0.560 m.; diameter of rim, 0.152 m.
About 475–450 B.C.

This type of stemless cup was produced during the period from 480 through the early fourth century B.C. It appears in figured ware as well. The Joslyn example is typical of black-glaze examples in its heaviness, lack of incised or impressed decoration, and the simple pattern on the undersurface. It served as a drinking vessel or a bowl.

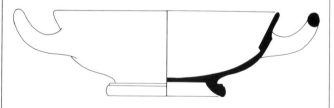

Figure 29. Profile of cup.

34. Attic Black-Glaze Lekanis

1945.66

Gift of Mrs. A. F. Jonas, 1945
Bowl: height, 0.360 m.; diameter, 0.070 m.; Lid: height,
  0.030 m.; diameter, 0.071 m.
About 425 B.C.

The lekanis is a small bowl, usually lidded. It served as a container for both objects, such as thread or toys, as well as for foods, such as spices. It was also commonly used as a toilet article and therefore as a bridal gift. Often it appears as a burial offering in graves.

Lekanides vary in size; the Joslyn example is of the smallest variety. Although there are lekanides with figural decoration, these enjoy their greatest popularity in the fourth century, while the black-glaze version is primarily a fifth century B.C. phenomenon.

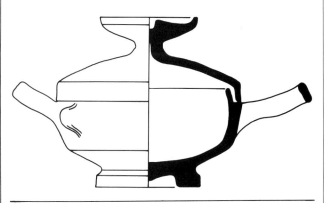

Figure 30. Profile of lekanis.

35. Italic Black-Glaze Askos

1945.65

Gift of Mrs. A. F. Jonas, 1945
Height, 0.111 m.; diameter of foot, 0.104 m.
Fourth century B.C.

In addition to imitating figural pottery (see Nos. 6, 37–39), fourth century Italian potters also imitated Attic black-glaze pottery. As with the figural pottery, black-glaze productions were essentially derivative of Attic examples.

The askos is one of the great number of shapes devoted to pouring and storing oil. To qualify as an askos, a vessel is wider than it is high, with a spout at one side of the top and a handle arching over to the other side. Note the narrow, flaring spout designed to control the flow of oil. This particular version is especially close to Attic models and appears in versions with figural decoration.

36. Italic Black-Glaze Bowl

1951.561

Gift of Mrs. W. H. Quigley, 1951
Height, 0.061 m.; diameter of rim, 0.170 m.
Fourth century B.C.

Bowls without handles were not popular before the late sixth century B.C.; because their shape seems to develop from that of dishes, it is likely that they were used for eating rather than drinking.

The outstanding feature of this bowl is the elaborate decoration on the interior. The presence of the central Gorgoneion recalls its appearance on Archaic bilingual cups such as No. 20. Note that by the fourth century the Gorgoneion is more feminine and therefore less frightening.

37. Apulian Red-Figure Pelike

For a discussion of this shape, see No. 6.

This is an especially high quality Apulian example; note the careful drawing of both figures and subsidiary decoration.

The genre scene on A has no specific mythological content: a woman sits in her boudoir, performing her toilette, with a male admirer on either side and a female attendant behind. She ties a scarf around her head and her maid will further adorn her with a wreath of laurel leaves. The chest which the maid holds probably contains clothes or jewelry. The male figure to the right holds a strigil, a curved instrument used by athletes to clean the skin. Here the context for a strigil is incongruous; it probably serves only as an attribute, indicating that the individual is a vigorous youth.

The artist attempts to show depth here, a difficult task in a two-dimensional medium such as vase-painting: he places the female attendant on an imaginary groundline above her mistress and the male admirers in order to suggest that she is in the background. This convention is one apparently developed by monumental wall-painters during the early fifth century B.C. and taken over by vase-painters shortly thereafter.

7.1984

On permanent loan from the Anthropology Division,
  University of Nebraska State Museum
Formerly in the collection of George W. Lininger, Omaha
Height, 0.450 m.; diameter, 0.300 m.
Attributed to a follower of the Dijon and Iliupersis Painters, very close in style to the earliest work of the Schlaepfer Painter. About 365–355 B.C.
A: A woman sits in her boudoir with admirers and attendant.
B: Two pairs of youths converse.

38. Apulian Red-Figure Skyphos

1957.111

Museum Purchase, 1957
Height, 0.121 m.; diameter of rim, 0.141 m.
Unattributed. About 375 B.C.
A: A woman holding a thyrsos stands near an altar.
B: A nude youth with staff holds a strigil.

Note how similar the shape of this skyphos is to the earlier Attic example, No. 32.

This piece has little, if any, narrative coherence. The female figure on A stands by an altar and carries a thyrsos, a wooden pole with ivy leaves tied at the top, which is ordinarily an attribute of Dionysiac figures. She may, then, be a maenad as seen on the Attic example, No. 21, although maenads do not usually appear alone. The figure on B, based on his nudity and the strigil which he holds, is probably an athlete, although the staff is ordinarily an attribute of trainers rather than athletes themselves. Clearly this painter uses figures for their decorative utility rather than to present coherent types or a developed narrative.

39. Apulian Red-Figure Bell-Krater

6.1984

On permanent loan from the Anthropology Division,
    University of Nebraska State Museum
Formerly in the collection of George W. Lininger, Omaha
Height, 0.380 m.; diameter, 0.248 m.
Attributed to the Group of the Painter of the Truro Pelike.
    About 340–320 B.C.
A: A female figure attends a seated Eros.
B: Two youths confront one another.

Note how the shape of the bell-krater has changed over time, becoming taller, slimmer, and more attenuated than the Attic prototype, No. 31.

No particular myth is represented here, although the subject is generally mythological. A female attendant holds a tambourine and a fan; Eros extends a bowl with fruit to her. Eros sits on a rocky seat; he is extremely effeminate, with an elaborate hairdo and decked with earrings, necklaces, and bracelets. Note how much more effeminate he is here than on the Attic cup, No. 30, more than a century earlier: he has moved from being the henchman of Aphrodite to an overt representation of androgynous sensuality.

The scene on the reverse is perfunctory. Halteres, or jumping weights, which were held by athletes during an event like our modern long jump, hang in the field; they are incongruous here, as the context is not athletic.

Note the addition of a yellow wash over the figures on this piece, giving it a more polychromous and more gaudy effect.

40. Gnathia Skyphos

1951.565

Gift of Mrs. W. H. Quigley, 1951
Height, 0.142 m.; diameter of rim, 0.119 m.
Attributed to the Laurel Spray Group. About 330–320 B.C.

Note that this shape has affinities to skyphoi in the black-glaze and figural repertories such as No. 38, although it is more attenuated here.

Gnathia ware is also produced in Apulia. It appears in the second quarter of the fourth century B.C., and production continues for about a century. It is named for the site where it was originally found, ancient Egnazia. Now scholars believe the center of production to have been the Greek city of Tarentum, from where it spread across Apulia and Campania and south into Sicily.

Decoration is primarily ornamental, consisting of geometric and floral designs rendered in red, yellow, and white on a dark painted background. Many examples do preserve figures as well. On the Joslyn skyphos the primary decoration on both sides consists of horizontal vines with vertical vines descending.

41. Apulian Volute-Krater

The volute-krater is a shape invented by Athenian potters more than 250 years earlier than this example; it derives its name from the spiral, scroll-like form at the top of the handles.

Apulian potters produced relief wares in addition to painted pottery. Note here the medallions preserving Gorgoneia which decorate the volutes on the handles; this is the same motif which appears in the bowl, No. 36, and much earlier on the Attic cup, No. 20. The slight protrusions which appear on either side of the roots of the handles are degenerate versions of swans' heads which appeared on earlier, more careful versions of the shape.

1961.572

Gift of Mr. and Mrs. Arthur Wiesenberger, 1961
Height to top of handle, 0.553 m.; diameter of shoulder,
   0.256 m.
About 325–275 B.C.

Shapes with Greek Names in the Exhibition

Alabastron: A flask, with an elongated body, rounded base, narrow neck, and flat lip, used to contain and pour oil; No. 3.

Amphora: A two-handled jar used for storing liquids, such as oil and water, and solids, such as grain; Nos. 7, 12.

A *Neck-Amphora* has the neck sharply set off from the body; Nos. 5, 16, 21, 23, 29.

Aryballos: A small flask, usually no more than 8 centimeters high, with narrow neck and flat lip, used to contain and pour oil; Nos. 9–11.

Askos: A flask which is wider than it is high, with a narrow mouth to one side at the top and a handle reaching across to the other side. It is used to contain and pour oil; No. 35.

Hydria: A jar with wide belly, narrow neck, and three handles: two are horizontal, for lifting, and one is vertical, for pouring. It is used to store and transport water; Nos. 4, 17.

Krater: A large, deep bowl with two handles, used for mixing wine and water.

A *Bell-krater* has horizontal handles and a bell-shaped body; Nos. 31, 39.

A *Column-krater* has vertical, columnar handles and a neck which is set off; No. 22.

A *Volute-krater* has vertical handles, which terminate in spirals, and a set-off neck; No. 41.

Kyathos: A dipper with one high-swung vertical handle, used as a ladle; No. 19.

Kylix: A drinking cup which has a shallow bowl, two horizontal handles, and a tall foot. The term "kylix" covers a wide variety of shapes, many of which are called simply "cups" or "bowls"; Nos. 8, 15, 18, 20, 30, 33.

Lekanis: A shallow basin with narrow ring foot, two handles, and a rim with a ledge to receive a lid; No. 34.

Lekythos: A slim jug with a narrow neck, one vertical handle, and a flat lip, used to contain and pour oil; Nos. 24–28.

Oinochoe: A pitcher with high vertical handle and trefoil mouth, used for pouring wine; No. 14.

Olpe: A tall pitcher with vertical handle and sagging belly; No. 13.

Pelike: A type of amphora with low, sagging belly: Nos. 6, 37.

Skyphos: A drinking cup with nearly vertical sides and horizontal handles; Nos. 32, 38, 40.

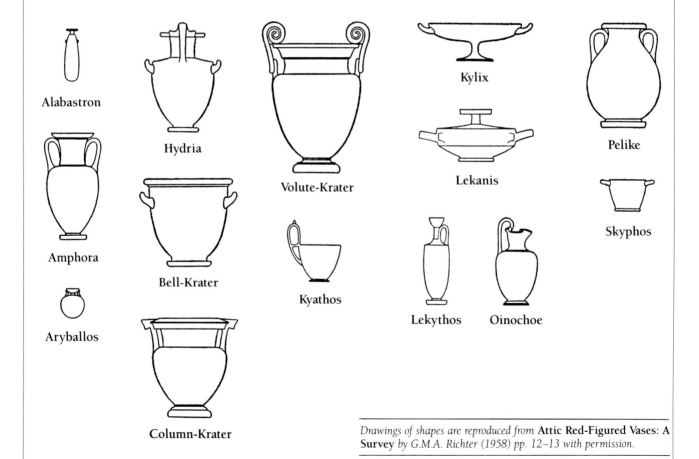

Alabastron · Hydria · Volute-Krater · Kylix · Pelike · Amphora · Bell-Krater · Kyathos · Lekanis · Lekythos · Oinochoe · Skyphos · Aryballos · Column-Krater

Drawings of shapes are reproduced from **Attic Red-Figured Vases: A Survey** *by G.M.A. Richter (1958) pp. 12–13 with permission.*

Glossary

Achilles: A Greek hero who excelled in the fighting at Troy. His dispute with Agamemnon, the leader of the Greeks, is the subject of the *Iliad*.

Bacchylides: A lyric poet (?524 B.C.–?) who wrote victory odes and choral odes, called dithyrambs, for successful participants in panhellenic contests.

Demosthenes: A master of rhetoric and legal procedure, held to be the greatest Athenian orator. (384–322 B.C.)

Diomedes: A Greek hero whose raging attacks on the Trojans form the subject of Book V of the *Iliad*.

Doric Order: The oldest and simplest of the orders of classical Greek architecture. The heavy fluted columns have no base and a cushion-shaped capital. The frieze, above the columns, consists of triglyphs (blocks decorated with three parallel vertical channels on the face) alternating with metopes (plain blocks, sometimes preserving sculptural decoration).

Hector: The greatest of the Trojan princes who is killed by Achilles in Book XXII of the *Iliad*.

Homer: A Greek epic poet, author of the *Iliad* and the *Odyssey*, who is believed to have lived in the eighth century B.C.

Iconography: The subject of a representation, as opposed to "style" or the manner in which the subject is rendered.

Iliad: An epic poem authored by Homer, concerning events in the tenth year of the Trojan War.

Mimnermus: A poet and musician of the seventh century B.C.

Nemean Games: Contests, primarily athletic, held at the site of Nemea in the northeast Peloponnese. Very similar to the Olympic Games, these became panhellenic in 573 B.C. The prize for victory was a crown of wild celery.

Odysseus: A Greek hero, known for his shrewdness and cunning, whose homecoming from Troy serves as the subject of the *Odyssey*.

Odyssey: An epic poem authored by Homer which deals with the homecoming of Odysseus after the fall of Troy.

Panhellenic: Anything which concerns or includes all Greeks as a group.

Pediment: A wide triangular space at the top of the facade of a building, which often was filled with sculpture.

Pelops: A legendary Greek hero for whom the Peloponnese (which translates "Island of Pelops") was named.

Phaedrus: A dialogue by Plato where Socrates discusses the nature of truth, beauty, and excellence.

Pindar: A lyric poet (518–438 B.C.) who wrote victory odes for successful participants in the contests at Delphi, Isthmia, Nemea, and Olympia.

Solon: An Athenian statesman and poet (c. 600 B.C.) who carried out legal and economic reforms.

Theocritus: A poet (c. 300–c. 260 (?) B.C.) of the Hellenistic period, best known for his bucolic works.

Tyrtaeus: A Spartan poet and military man of the seventh century B.C.

Doric Order

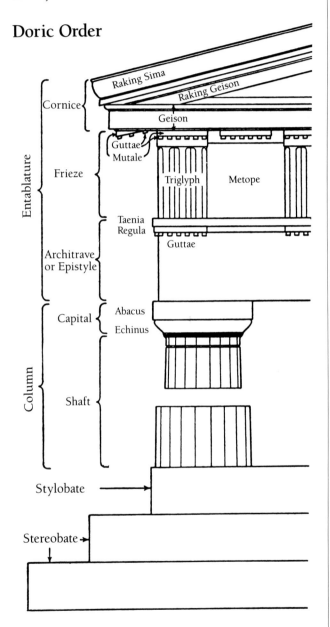

Figure 31. Elevation of the Doric order. Reproduced from **Greek Temples** *by I. H. Grinnell (1943) p. xviii with permission.*

Chronological Chart

Note: The chronological chart is adapted with permission of the author from *Ancient Greek Literature and Society* (Doubleday, 1975) by Charles Rowan Beye. The chart purposely provides more historical and literary information than the discussions in the text of the catalogue. The additional information is here for the benefit of those readers who wish to see connections between developments in art, literature, and history in more detail than the scope of this catalogue allows.

BRONZE AGE
(3000–1100 B.C.)

c.2000–1450 Minoan dominance of the Mediterranean

c.1450–1200 Mycenaean dominance of the Mediterranean

c.1180 Troy destroyed

***Mycenaean pottery derived from Minoan prototypes; exported widely

DARK AGE
(1100–900 B.C.)

c.1000 Dorian invasion

***Protogeometric pottery produced at Athens and elsewhere

GEOMETRIC PERIOD
(900–700 B.C.)

800–700 Beginnings of colonization in Sicily

***Invention of the alphabet

***Homer (or whoever he or they were) composing *Iliad, Odyssey*

***Geometric pottery produced at Athens and other centers

ORIENTALIZING PERIOD
(700–600 B.C.)

700–600 Colonization of west continues

c.650–600 Spread of tyrant governments in Greece

c.640–630 Standardized coinage begins in Asia Minor and adopted by Greek city-states

***Tyrtaeus writing poetry in Sparta in the second half of the century

c.630 Mimnermus writing poetry in Asia Minor

c.612 Sappho born in Mytilene on Lesbos

***Corinthian pottery dominates artistically and commercially

***Black-figure technique develops

***Western and Eastern Greece imitate mainland pottery

***Etruscan bucchero produced

ARCHAIC PERIOD
(600–480 B.C.)

594/3 Solon appointed chief magistrate at Athens to reform the constitution

May 8, 585 An eclipse predicted by Thales

561 Peisistratos becomes tyrant at Athens

c.535 Thespis wins first prize when tragedy first introduced at the Greater Dionysia in Athens

c.600 Athenian potters imitate Corinthian wares and black-figure technique

c.575 Athenian pottery displaces Corinthian pottery artistically and commercially

c.530 Red-figure technique develops at Athens

525 Aeschylus born at Athens

c.524 Bacchylides born on Ceos

518 Pindar born in Boeotia

510 Tyrants expelled from Athens

508 Cleisthenes begins his reforms of the Athenian constitution

c.500 satyr plays are added to the Tragic Festival at Athens

c.495 Perikles, Sophocles born at Athens

***Herodotus said to have been born "before the Persian War" at Halicarnassus

490 Persians invade Greece; defeated at Marathon

c.490 Pheidias born

488/7 comedy introduced at the Greater Dionysia festival

c.485 Euripides born at Athens

484 Aeschylus' first victory

CLASSICAL PERIOD
(480–400 B.C.)

480 Xerxes enters Greece; battle of Thermopylae; battle of Salamis a great Greek victory

479 Battle of Plataea: Greeks victorious, Persians withdraw

476 Pindar writes *Olympian I*, Bacchylides writes *Ode V*

469 Socrates born

468 Sophocles defeats Aeschylus at tragic festival

between 460–455 Thucydides born at Athens

456 Aeschylus dies at Gela in Sicily

455 Euripides first competes at the Dionysia

c.455 Aristophanes born at Athens

c.475 Significant production of Attic black-glaze begins; white-ground funerary lekythoi appear

454 Growth of Athenian imperialism evident; general Perikles becomes a dominant force in Athenian politics

444 Herodotus goes to assist in the founding of Thurii in Southern Italy

447 Parthenon is begun

c.444 South Italian production of red-figure and black-glaze begins

438 Pindar dies

432 Assembly of Dorians at Sparta decide on war with Athens

432 Parthenon is completed

430 Plague at Athens

429 Perikles dies

429 Plato born at Athens

c.428 publication of Herodotus' *Histories*

424 Thucydides goes into exile

421 Peace of Nikias between Athens and Sparta

c.420 Herodotus dies

94

413 Athenian defeat at Syracuse in Sicily

405 Battle of Aegospotamoi; Athens' fleet destroyed

404 Surrender of Athens

406 Euripides dies in Macedonia, Sophocles dies at Athens

404 Thucydides returns to Athens

FOURTH CENTURY
(400–323 B.C.)

400–350 Greek states battle for dominant position

356 Alexander born in Macedonia

336 Alexander succeeds Philip to the Macedonian throne

323 Alexander dies; his successors divide his kingdom

304 Ptolemy declares himself King in Egypt

399 Socrates dies at Athens

387 Plato starts the Academy at Athens

384 Aristotle is born in Chalcidice

347 Plato dies at Athens

342/1 Menander born at Athens

335 Aristotle comes to Athens, founds school

c.300 Theocritus born in Alexandria

*** Attic and South Italian red-figure and black-glaze production continues

Bibliography

The following works served as general references for the authors of this catalogue. We recommend this list to those who wish to investigate the ancient Greek past further.

Beye, C. R. *Ancient Greek Literature and Society* (1975)

Biers, W. *The Archaeology of Greece* (1980)

Boardman, J. *Athenian Black Figure Vases* (1974)

———. *Athenian Red Figure Vases: The Archaic Period* (1975)

Carpenter, R. *The Humanistic Value of Archaeology* (1933)

Cook, R. M. *Greek Painted Pottery* (1972)

Coulton, J. J. *Ancient Greek Architects at Work: Problems of Structure and Design* (1977)

Hood, S. *The Arts in Prehistoric Greece* (1978)

Kitto, H. *The Greeks* (1957)

Noble, J. *The Techniques of Painted Attic Pottery* (1965)

Perry, B. E. "The Early Greek Capacity for Viewing Things Separately," *Transactions of the American Philological Society* 68 (1937) 403–427.

Pollitt, J. *Art and Experience in Classical Greece* (1972)

GAUL

ITALY

R. Arno

Populonia
ETRURIA
Arretium
Vetulonia
Vulci
Tarquinia
Caere
Rome
R. Tiber
Cales
CAMPANIA
APULIA
Herculaneum
Pompeii
LUCANIA
Paestum
Egnazia
Tarentum

MACEDONIA

THESSALY

GREECE

TYRRHENIAN
SEA

Corinth
Athens
PELOPONNESUS
LACONIA

Aegean Sea

Perg
IO

Eph

Sam

Spo

SICILY

MEDITERRANEAN

Carthage

Syracuse

Knossos
CRETE

NORTH
AFRICA